The Idea of a Christian Society
and Other Writings

BY T. S. ELIOT

THE COMPLETE POEMS AND PLAYS OF T. S. ELIOT

Verse

COLLECTED POEMS 1909–1962
FOUR QUARTETS
THE WASTE LAND & OTHER POEMS
THE WASTE LAND
A facsimile and transcript of the original drafts
SELECTED POEMS

Children's Verse

OLD POSSUM'S BOOK OF PRACTICAL CATS

Plays

COLLECTED PLAYS
MURDER IN THE CATHEDRAL
THE FAMILY REUNION
THE COCKTAIL PARTY
THE CONFIDENTIAL CLERK
THE ELDER STATESMAN

Literary Criticism

SELECTED ESSAYS
THE USE OF POETRY *and* THE USE OF CRITICISM
TO CRITICIZE THE CRITIC
ON POETRY AND POETS
FOR LANCELOT ANDREWES
SELECTED PROSE OF T. S. ELIOT

Social Criticism

THE IDEA OF A CHRISTIAN SOCIETY
NOTES TOWARDS THE DEFINITION OF CULTURE

THE IDEA OF
A CHRISTIAN SOCIETY
and Other Writings

T. S. ELIOT

With an Introduction by
DAVID L. EDWARDS

faber and faber

First published by Faber and Faber Limited in 1939
This edition first published in 1982
by Faber and Faber Limited
3 Queen Square London WC1N 3AU
Printed in Great Britain by
Fakenham Press Limited, Fakenham, Norfolk
All rights reserved

British Library Cataloguing in Publication Data

Eliot, T. S.
The idea of a Christian society and other writings.
1. Sociology, Christian
I. Title   II. Edwards, David L.
261   BV625

ISBN 0-571-18069-8
ISBN 0-571-11891-7 Pbk

Contents

Introduction

THE lectures which T. S. Eliot delivered at Cambridge in March
1939 and published as *The Idea of a Christian Society* in October
1939 have received less attention than most of his writings. As a
long line of studies already attests, he is generally agreed to have
been second to none among poets writing in English during the
first three-quarters of the twentieth century; to have led a revolution in his reassessments of the English literary tradition; and to
have been not unworthy of the Nobel Prize, of the Order of
Merit and of that pinnacle where the cultured public in the
English-speaking world placed him for some twenty years
before his death in 1965 (mostly without accepting his intellectual position). He is also generally agreed to have been a great
gentleman, and a Christian in the self-discipline of his private life
as well as in his poetry's unforgettable expression of an austere
faith. In fact Eliot's general importance in English intellectual
history places him alongside John Dryden, Samuel Johnson,
S. T. Coleridge and Matthew Arnold, whose views of poetry and
life he discussed often and perceptively. However, despite the
publication of Roger Kojecky's valuable study of *T. S. Eliot's
Social Criticism* (1971), his role as prophet or sage has not yet been
taken as seriously as Coleridge's or Arnold's. In addition to the
stern judges cited by Dr Kojecky, Stephen Spender, for example,
was dismissive: 'On the whole, Eliot's social-religious activities
make one reflect on how extraordinarily ineffective the Church
of England has been in bringing Christian principles to bear on
political life.'[1] The best book so far published on Eliot relegated
'the Christian philosopher and politics' to an appendix, assessing

[1] Stephen Spender, *Eliot* (London: Fontana, 1975), p. 230.

9

him as 'not a political philosopher', rather as 'an absolutist, with the absolutism of the Christian faith' but 'not, quite deliberately not, a worldly or a humane way of looking at things'.[2] An Anglican monk who is an admirer of Eliot's has called *The Idea of a Christian Society* 'something of an artificial exercise in social theorizing'.[3] 'The most that can be said', writes a Cambridge historian who would have welcomed a full defence of conservative values, 'is that Eliot posed problems.'[4]

Obviously it would be absurd to claim for Eliot's 'social-religious activities' anything like the importance granted to his poetry and literary criticism. In *The Idea of a Christian Society* he repeatedly apologized for his inability to discuss sociology, politics or economics, and that was more than a conventional ploy intended to charm critics. In 1961 he delivered a lecture reviewing his literary criticism, and when this was published with other writings after his death four years later (in *To Criticize the Critic*), it was explained that 'had he lived he would have written a similar review of his sociological writings'. We note that he had not reckoned self-criticism in this field urgent. It is clear that much of the real interest of his 'social-religious activities' lies in their value to the student who would enter the field of poetry where he was the master. The contempt for the materialist world declaimed in *The Rock*; the dramatization of the Church's resistance to the State in *Murder in the Cathedral*; the vision of the English past 'folded in a single party' in 'East Coker' and 'Little Gidding'; the hope that England's life could be purged by the 'flame of incandescent terror' together with the admission of the inarticulateness of words and the ineffectiveness of activity; and the argument of the verse dramas from *The Family Reunion* that in modern England the road to holiness was very costly and often lonely, although still possible—all these

[2] A. D. Moody, *Thomas Stearns Eliot: Poet* (Cambridge: CUP, 1979), pp. 319–26.

[3] Martin Jarrett-Kerr, CR, in Graham Martin (ed.), *Eliot in Perspective* (London: Macmillan, 1970), p. 244.

[4] Maurice Cowling, *Religion and Public Doctrine in Modern England* (Cambridge: CUP, 1981), p. 120.

themes are expounded in the social writings. To an extent greater than is true of his master Dante (or of John Milton, to whom he found it difficult to do justice), Eliot when commenting on society impresses chiefly by implying a commentary on poems which now belong to the heritage of the English-speaking world.

But is that illumination of great poetry the only permanent value of these writings?

One must admit that *The Idea of a Christian Society* is to some extent a period piece. Near the beginning is to be found a tribute to 'Christian sociologists' who 'criticize the economic system in the light of Christian ethics'. This refers to writers such as V. A. Demant, who condemned British capitalism as it operated or was believed to operate in the 1930s, and who opposed to this an essentially medieval idea of 'Christendom'. But the economic analysis was not authoritative, and the ideal was one which no reputable thinker of the 1980s would think realistic. Such criticism of Britain was at the time thought to have so many merits that Eliot conceded that 'the defenders of the totalitarian system can make out a plausible case for maintaining that what we have is not democracy, but financial oligarchy.' But this was not the standard hatred of capitalism or Fascism to be found on the Left. Before the outbreak of war Eliot failed to appreciate the demonic character of Nazism. The 'dislike of everything maintained by Germany and/or Russia' was described as 'a compost of newspaper sensations and prejudice', and a British Fascist, General Fuller, 'has as good a title to call himself "a believer in democracy" as anyone else'. The 'German national religion' propagated by the Nazis was thought to be 'an eccentricity which is after all no odder than some cults held in Anglo-Saxon countries' and 'objections to oppression and violence and cruelty' were, despite strong feelings, rated as 'objectives to means not ends'. As for Britain's future: Eliot called for radical changes, but seems to have had no inkling of the imminence of the Labour Party's triumph after the war. 'I do not anticipate—short of some at present unpredictable revolution—the rise in Britain of a lower middle class political hierarchy. . . .' The claim of Socialism to be the necessary embodiment of social justice was not considered, and a Socialist such as H. J. Laski could be left with the impression that 'at bottom the Christian society of which Mr Eliot writes so eloquently is not a means of liberating the masses, but a technique of escape for a few chosen souls who cannot bear the general spectacle of civilization in decay.'[5] Certainly fellow-citizens who were in fact likely to be Labour voters were categorized unfavourably in *The Idea of a Christian Society*. 'The tendency of unlimited industrialism is to create bodies of men and women—of all classes—detached from tradition, alienated from religion, and susceptible to mass suggestion: in other words, a mob. And a mob will be no less a mob if it is to be well fed, well clothed, well housed and well disciplined.' Mainly because of this blindness to lower-middle-class and working-class resentments, the social exclusiveness of the Church of England did not trouble Eliot. Although he believed that 'the idea of Christian society ... can only be realized, in England, through the Church of England,' he declared that 'the danger of a National Church becoming a class Church, is not one that concerns us immediately today.' Moreover, he was no ecumenist. While not excluding the desirability of reunion one day, he referred only vaguely to Roman Catholicism and to the Free Churches in England.

Hindsight makes all these judgments look silly, and unfortunately their expression was not confined to *The Idea of a Christian Society*. Eliot wrote in the *Criterion* in October 1938: 'To understand thoroughly what is wrong with agriculture is to understand what is wrong with nearly everything else: with the domination of Finance, with our ideas and system of Education, indeed our whole philosophy of life.... What is fundamentally wrong is the *urbanization* of mind.... It is necessary that the greater part of the population of all classes (so long as we have classes) should be settled in the country and dependent upon it. One sees no hope either in the Labour Party or in the

---

[5] Leonard Unger (ed.), *T. S. Eliot: A Selected Critique*, 2nd edn. (New York: Rinehart, 1957), p. 42. This volume includes many other complaints about Eliot's lack of respect for the people.

equally unimaginative dominant section of the Conservative Party. There seems no hope in contemporary politics at all.' He was for a time interested in the pseudo-economic theory of 'Social Credit' and remained closely associated with the *New English Weekly* which had been started by sympathizers (more or less critical) with that theory. He was also identified with the group of 'Christian sociologists', many of whom had dabbled in Social Credit before adopting the more theological ideal of Christendom. He contributed to *Prospect for Christendom*, edited by Maurice Reckitt in 1945, and although his contribution was on 'Cultural Forces in the Human Order' he cannot entirely escape the condemnation which the group has received for its lack of economic understanding and theological maturity. Some of its own members, including V. A. Demant, lived to regret its Utopianism.[6] Obsessed by his beliefs that many governments were more or less equally at fault in the light of Christian ethics, and that 'at least a few men of letters should remain isolated' from partisan protests, he had refused to condemn the Nazi and Fascist armed intervention to support Franco in the Spanish Civil War and had condemned Oxford University for refusing to send a delegation to celebrations at Götingen, a university from which Jewish academics had been dismissed. Articles in the *Criterion* had shown the appeal to Eliot of the right-wing politics of the French writer Charles Maurras. In 1928 Eliot wrote: 'If anything, in another generation or so, is to preserve us from a sentimental Anglo-Fascism, it will be some system of ideas which will have gained much from the study of Maurras'—an unfortunate tribute to pay to one who was a royalist disowned by the Pretender to the French throne, an upholder of the social

[6] See D. L. Munby, *Christianity and Economic Problems* (London: Macmillan, 1956), and Ronald H. Preston, *Religion and the Persistence of Capitalism* (London: SCM, 1979). These criticized the Christendom group severely. The fullest statement of Demant's case was offered in *Religion and the Decline of Capitalism* (London: Faber, 1952). John Oliver provided an outline of social thought in the Church of England, 1918–39, in *The Church and Social Order* (Oxford: Mowbray, 1968). Wider surveys, from very different points of view, include Maurice Reckitt, *Maurice to Temple: a Century of the Social Movement in the Church of England*, 2nd edn. (London: Faber, 1957), and Edward Norman, *Church and Society in England 1770–1970* (Oxford: OUP, 1976).

position of the Church condemned by the Papacy, and an extremist condemned to life imprisonment after the war. And a lack of understanding of local religious realities, and of the convictions of non-Anglican Protestants, was disclosed in the course of Eliot's participation in the Anglo-Catholic agitation in the 1940s against the formation of the Church of South India. In the title of a pamphlet he summed up this coming together of Christians vastly outnumbered by Hindus as 'reunion by destruction'.

To be human is to err. However, it would be extraordinarily foolish to think that a man of this intellectual and spiritual stature, with a poet's passion for the precise use of words, was totally imprisoned in these judgments which history has mocked.

Lecturing in 1939, Eliot showed how troubled he was in conscience by this involvement in the British form of capitalism, and if he turned to Social Credit or to the Christendom group in order to gain glimpses of an alternative economy, surely we ought to acknowledge that being disturbed about the ethics of British capitalism in the 1930s was no mistake. The concern for the unemployed shown in *The Rock* was inevitable in a Christian. The only mistake would have been to persist in loyalty to an inexpert panacea, and we should note that Eliot (who was himself thoroughly urbanized) overcame his identification with Social Credit or the Christendom group to the extent of ceasing to criticize economic policy in public and investing his savings through his brother-in-law, a stockbroker. He could adopt an innocent tone of ignorance about economics, but he had, after all, held a responsible job in a bank for eight years. In a review of a book by Karl Mannheim (a sociologist who fascinated him) in the *Spectator* in June 1940, Eliot announced that 'society cannot return to any earlier degree of simplicity.' Even in *The Idea of a Christian Society* he rejected the plea for 'a simple mode of life, scrapping all the constructions of the modern world that we can bring ourselves to dispense with', as 'Utopian'. Not all ecologists of a later generation showed this degree of realism.

As early as 1928, in an article on 'The Literature of Fascism' in the *Criterion*, Eliot attacked Fascism as 'a form of faith which is solely appropriate to a religion'. He often said that he could not be a Fascist because he was a Christian, and indeed his whole work shows that he hated any smell of power.[7] His final judgment on Maurras—whose royalism pre-dated Fascism and who was anti-German—was that he ought to have confined himself to literature; his *Action Française* had merely increased political and religious animosities while discouraging the spread of 'those of his ideas which were sound and strong'. When the war against Hitler and Mussolini came, Eliot shared the English patriotism of the time fully (although never hysterically) and expressed it nobly. In his introduction to *A Choice of Kipling's Verse* (1941) he wrote about another poet, like him not born in England, whose 'historical imagination' had been fired; and he even commended an imperialism which previously he had despised. After the war his calls for the restoration of the European cultural community (as in the talks appended to *Notes towards the Definition of Culture*, 1948) won a respectful attention which would never have been given to one tainted with Fascism.

It cannot be denied that Eliot was more cautious about the ideas of the Left than about those of the Right. It was no accident that *The Idea of a Christian Society* was delivered as lectures at the invitation of the Cambridge college most noted for its political conservatism (Corpus Christi). In the *Christian News-Letter* of 21 March 1945 (under the pen-name 'Metoikos') Eliot argued that support of the 1944 White Paper on Full Employment was probably right on humanitarian grounds but was not necessarily binding on the Christian conscience: 'we may say generally that it is the duty of the individual to do what he can in his own sphere of action.' Nor can it be denied that writing more important than that hesitant contribution included touches of snobbery. The dance around the bonfire was not merriment in which he joined,

---

[7] William M. Chace contrasted *The Political Identities of Ezra Pound and T. S. Eliot* (Stanford: Stanford University Press, 1973). Eliot's 1933 paper on 'Catholicism and International Order', also attacking Fascism, was reprinted in *Essays Ancient and Modern* (London: Faber, 1936).

and a suffocatingly small social world was presented in his drawing-room plays. It is also clear, however, that his religion taught him that God had made, and Christ had died for, 'ordinary people'—and that his work showed an increasingly mature appreciation of the implications of this belief, until the peace of the close of *The Elder Statesman* (1957). Already in 1939 he was, he tells us, 'deeply indebted' to the works of Jacques Maritain, the French Catholic thinker who influenced many by his positive attitudes to the Republic and to the Left, who was found congenial by Archbishop William Temple, and who lived long enough to inspire the far from reactionary social thought of Pope Paul VI. Eliot also paid compliments to the scholarly saint of English Christian Socialism, R. H. Tawney.

Although he was a churchwarden of St Stephen's, Gloucester Road, in London for a quarter of a century from 1934, and even a lodger in its vicarage until the war, and always maintained a lifestyle of a semi-clerical cut, it would be grossly inaccurate to regard Eliot as an Anglican bigot, loudly beating an antique drum. While editor of the *Criterion* he welcomed a wide range of contributors, including Communists. As a publisher he worked very happily with colleagues, and was eager to encourage authors, who were not devout. He never allowed the reprinting of the only book of his which was uncharitable propaganda (*After Strange Gods*, 1934), and he came to regard the hero of his *Family Reunion* (a play containing elements of autobiography, first performed in the month when he delivered *The Idea of a Christian Society* as lectures) as 'an insufferable prig'. His 'quotable' description of himself as 'classicist in literature, royalist in politics and anglo-catholic in religion' (in the Preface to *For Lancelot Andrewes*, 1928) was 'provoked' by the experience of being challenged by his former teacher, Irving Babbitt, to 'come out into the open' about his recent baptism; but by 1961 'I should not be inclined to express it in quite this way.' 'My religious beliefs are unchanged,' he then declared, 'and I am strongly in favour of the maintenance of the monarchy in all countries which have a monarchy'—but he declined to grow small enough to be covered by a label. And to some extent he made up for his former lack of ecumenical zeal by his friendships with several leading Roman Catholics and Free Churchmen and by his sensitive discussion of 'Sect and Cult' in *Notes towards the Definition of Culture*. In that book is also to be found a more mature reflection on the English class system, which has been so bound up with the English denominational divisions. The lack of any systematic exposition of his religious beliefs is a reminder that he was never a theologian or preacher (as his grandfather had been, dominating the religious life of St Louis until his death in 1887). Eliot had no interest in developing the commentary on the utterances of bishops which he began sketchily in *Thoughts after Lambeth* (1931), or in writing more plays for performance in church after *Murder in the Cathedral* (1935). He remained a layman, and inside the eminent churchman whose patrons included King George VI and Bishop George Bell the poet never quite died who in a poem of 1917 had compared the institutional Church with a hippopotamus. This pillar of orthodoxy, whose prose assured his readers that religion ought to be dogmatic not liberal, revealed not natural, wrote in one of his most solemn, beautiful and deservedly famous statements, in 1941:

> For most of us, there is only the unattended
> Moment, the moment in and out of time,
> The distraction fit, lost in a shaft of sunlight,
> The wild thyme unseen, or the winter lightning
> Or the waterfall, or music heard so deeply
> That it is not heard at all, but you are the music
> While the music lasts. These are only hints and guesses,
> Hints followed by guesses; and the rest
> Is prayer, observance, discipline, thought and action.
> The hint half guessed, the gift half understood, is Incarnation.

But how strong were Eliot's central social teachings? More serious than the problem of relatively minor defects in a poet's opinions during the 1930s is the question whether he erred by dreaming of a society in which the Church of England would enjoy many of the privileges of the Nazi, Fascist and Communist

Parties in other countries. The dream is so obviously absurd that it seems incredible that the author of *The Waste Land* and *Ash-Wednesday* should have entertained it. Yet we find Stephen Spender summing up *The Idea of a Christian Society*: 'Eliot confines himself in this book to discussing the idea of the Christian State in England, which seems the last country in Europe where it would be likely to be adopted—the English being averse to the idea of being dominated by the Church.' Spender goes on to poke fun at the 'Christianly muscular and co-operative' people with whom Eliot had discussed, and went on discussing, the suggestions here presented. He speaks of them as 'forever plotting to set up cells and to penetrate every branch of the community with their redemptive schemes; clergymen, dons and intellectuals asking one another, anxiously sometimes indeed, whether they were not in danger of acting as a kind of spiritual Gestapo or Communist cell.' He then seems to check himself, recalling who it is who is said to have been involved in this dottiness. 'What is moving about Eliot's social writings is the way in which he sets the cat of the Holy Spirit among the pigeons of all existing politics. . . . One may suppose that Eliot's Christian social thinking is a self-imposed task of discipline and humility: rejection of the view that came so easily to him that the modern world can be dismissed as the decadence of the civilization. . . .'[8]

The first comment that must be made is that Spender's description of Eliot's associates is a travesty of the discussions held by people of high and painful integrity in the small fellowships known as the Moot and the Christian Frontier Council. In particular it fails to emphasize that Eliot was outspoken in his private warnings against the adoption of any kind of political programme, however benevolent.[9]

The Idea of a Christian Society deserves to be read with care, to see how far its tendency is totalitarian, particularly since Spender was not unique when exaggerating this element because of his

---

[8] Spender, *Eliot*, pp. 230–7.
[9] The main facts were set out by Roger Kojecky in *T. S. Eliot's Social Criticism* (London: Faber, 1971), pp. 156–97.

suspicion of Eliot's Christian friends. An American critic has concluded that 'Eliot's religious "control and balance", in spite of minor concessions, are very nearly total: statesmen and teachers would be forced to conform to Christian dogma, and dissentients would be held to a minimum.... Whatever reforms were required would be required not because they improved people's lives but because they coincided with Christian doctrine....'[10] But in these lectures Eliot did not recommend 'any particular political form'; he was simply advocating 'whatever State is suitable to a Christian Society'. Nor did he advocate a State 'in which the rulers are chosen because of their qualifications, still less their eminence as Christians'. Christianity is not to be imposed on the people by the government; on the contrary, the 'temper and traditions of the people' ought to be sufficiently Christian to impose on the politicians 'a Christian framework within which to realize their ambitions and advance the prosperity and prestige of their country'. This implies an understanding of party politics much more sceptical than the ideology behind the formation of 'Christian' parties such as the Catholic parties of the 1930s or the post-war Christian Democrats. The education of the intellectually able should 'primarily train people to think in Christian categories, though it could not compel belief and would not impose the necessity for insincere profession of belief'. The activity of non-Christian teachers would be both inevitable and a benefit to intellectual vitality. The organization of the life of the mass of the people should lessen the present 'conflict between what is easy for them and what their circumstances dictate and what is Christian'—not, it should be noted, impose Christian belief or behaviour. Surely elements of liberalism ought to be detected in this picture of the Christian society, and they are in keeping with Eliot's habitual and often expressed mistrust of the State and of politicians. He once wrote that 'a rational government would be one ... which did as little governing as possible'. As we shall see,

---

[10] Allen Austin, *T. S. Eliot: The Literary and Social Criticism* (Bloomington, Ind.: Indiana University Press, 1971), p. 79.

this caution was such that at least one distinguished friend and fellow-Christian publicly accused him in 1939 of wanting a 'Sub-Christian Society', with too much emphasis on the material welfare of the people.

Eliot could not see how the Church 'can ever accept as a permanent settlement one law for itself and another for the world'. Such a sentence alarms those who smell the Inquisition's smoke in any cloud of incense. It is certainly not a complete answer to what was admitted to be the 'very difficult problem' of the Church's attitude to legislation contrary to Christian principles. But Eliot, while he advocated 'a hierarchical organization in direct and official relation with the State' and believed that the Church must speak as 'the final authority within the nation' (presumably through the hierarchy) in 'matters of dogma, matters of faith and morals', was none the less on his guard against entrusting too much power to State-supported bishops. He advocated a 'Community of Christians ... composed of both clergy and laity, of the more spiritually and intellectually developed of both'—a teaching body distinct from the hierarchy. This very loosely 'composed' community would, however, also be corruptible, and in a postscript Eliot printed a theologian's alarm at the implied élitism. He continued to worry about what was desirable, sometimes favouring the idea of a small lay 'order' composed of persons as monkish as he was himself. He was clear that Christian intellectuals were needed to counteract the tendency of the mass of the people 'to identify the Church with the actual hierarchy and to suspect it of being an instrument of oligarchy and class'. Seeking other checks on the official Church leadership, he urged that 'the allegiance of the individual to his own Church is secondary to his allegiance to the Universal Church' and he believed that a tension between Church and State was an essential distinguishing mark of the Christian society. Church leaders speaking on 'mixed' questions of faith and politics should speak only as individuals—which would seem to set limits on what is elsewhere defined as the duty of the Church to contest 'heretical opinion or immoral legislation and administration'. If we ask what Eliot meant by that duty, we find that it is hard to tell in these lectures when he was thinking about England and when about Europe. Much of the 'immoral legislation' which he would have Church leaders 'contest' was not legislation about matters such as divorce or abortion (which he did not discuss), but the law of a regime presided over by Hitler or Stalin. There is no reason why we should jump to the conclusion that Eliot ever wanted for Church leaders an absolute dominance, forcing the people to conform to Christian dogma.

In *The Idea of a Christian Society* as in *Murder in the Cathedral*, the Church was seen as 'shielding the community against tyranny' and not as being tyrannical itself. To adapt Spender's own phrases, Eliot was so well aware that the truly Christian life was one of 'discipline and humility' that he wished to set the cat of the Holy Spirit among all plump ecclesiastical pigeons, official or intellectual, as well as among politicians of all shapes and sizes. It may well be the case that in this strikingly incomplete sketch of the Christian society the restrictions which he explicitly envisaged on the institutional Church's position were inadequate, but we should note his own words of 1937: 'only in humility, charity and purity—most of all perhaps in humility—can we be prepared to receive the grace of God without which human operations are vain.' We should also note his words of 1939: 'I cannot foresee any future society in which we could classify Christians and non-Christians simply by their professions of belief, or even, by any rigid code, by their behaviour.... Some who would vigorously repudiate Christianity are more Christian than many who maintain it.' This was a significant admission, coming from one who had written in the 1937 symposium on *Revelation*: 'The division between those who accept and those who deny Christian revelation, I take to be the most profound difference between human beings.'

In a sympathetic review of Eliot's social criticism, Raymond Williams was surely right to claim that 'the bleakness, which is a kind of discipline, is wholly salutary. If Eliot, when read attentively, has the effect of checking the complacencies of liberalism, he has also, when read critically, the effect of making complacent conservatism impossible.'[11] Indeed, it could be argued that the real tragedy of Eliot's social criticism was that he did not do more of it, having studied sociology, politics and economics at a greater depth.

He might have developed into a Christian Conservative philosopher, balancing the Christian Socialists who have dominated the Church's thought since the publication of William Temple's *Christianity and Social Order* in 1942. Since he did not do so the possibility is difficult to imagine, but it is surely significant that the *Criterion*, the 'literary review' which he had edited industriously since 1922, had contained an increasing number of articles on politics and economics with his own 'Commentaries'—and that when he closed it down in January 1939 his 'Last Words' confirmed that his main interests had left literature. Presumably the ending of this quarterly gave Eliot the time needed to prepare *The Idea of a Christian Society* with its plea for 'a discussion which must occupy many minds for a long time to come'. When introducing a volume of Eliot's *Selected Prose* in 1953, John Hayward, in whose London apartment Eliot was then living, wrote that 'his critical faculties have been increasingly exercised in recent years on social problems'—adding that he might well feel that he had accomplished as much as he could in literary criticism.

Had Eliot with his growing prestige concentrated on social problems, he might have made the materialism prevailing in Conservative policies less secure. Since the 1940s many Conservative politicians have been Christians in their private lives, many churchgoers have voted Conservative, and there have been some thoughtful remarks about the relevance of religion (among statesmen, most notably from Lord Hailsham); but there has been no systematic attempt to relate Christian principles to the problems facing the Conservative Party. In the context of English history since the seventeenth century, this is remarkable. However, the restoration of the old alliance between the Tory Party and the Church of England was not to

---

[11] Raymond Williams, *Culture and Society 1780–1950* (Harmondsworth: Penguin, 1961), p. 238.

be Eliot's vocation. His earlier strictures on Coleridge and Arnold for dissipating their gifts on political or cultural journalism seem to have been applied by his conscience to himself, with the result that his lecture on 'The Literature of Politics' at the Conservative Political Centre in 1955 was a tame affair. He returned to his aloofness, and his prophetic mantle was not passed to anyone else.[12]

Having considered the allegation that the tendency of Eliot's social criticism was totalitarian rather than gently conservative, we may turn to the accusation that he absurdly exaggerated the role of religion in society.

Since the Second World War in England Christians have shared with non-Christians a conviction that it is healthy for the State to recognize and respect the existence among its citizens of different religious and moral traditions or of agnosticism or atheism. The regularly churchgoing element in the population has dwindled to little more than a tenth of the whole; immigrants from countries which have never been even nominally Christian have settled down and multiplied; and the expression of scepticism about all religious beliefs, and about traditional Christian ethics, has been open and widely persuasive. Since our society is democratic the notion that the State ought to enforce the Church of England's traditional teaching on sexual morality, for example, has been abandoned; indeed, the Church of England often seems to have abandoned that teaching itself. At the same time as the Established Church and other religious institutions have declined in social significance in England, thoughtful English Christians have taken note of three facts: first, under many oppressive regimes the best elements in the Church are pitted against the State, with a strong theology advocating the liberation of the people and with shining examples of heroism including martyrdom; second, even in nations such as India where the Christian minority has not been in open conflict with the government the aim of that minority

[12] Anthony Quinton delivered the T. S. Eliot Lectures on the religious and secular traditions of conservative thought in England under the title *The Politics of Imperfection* (London: Faber, 1978).

has been to serve a 'secular' State in the pursuit of justice along-side fellow-citizens who adhere to non-Christian religions; and third, in the USA, where churchgoing is far more popular than it is in England, and 'In God We Trust' appears on the coinage, the separation of Church and State is an axiom of public policy. All these influences have contributed to the eclipse of the 'idea' which Eliot championed—as may be seen, for example, in D. L. Munby's Riddell Memorial Lectures on 'The Idea of a Secular Society and its Significance for Christians' (1963).

Munby granted that Eliot's idea made some sense against its historical background. 'There were good grounds in the thirties for believing that "neutral societies" were doomed to disappear before the crusading zeal of Communism and Fascism, as one such disappeared in the Spanish Civil War; the strongest grounds for such beliefs were to be found in the incompetence, credulity, and supineness of "liberal" leaders, the exceptions being the vigour of Roosevelt, whose effective impact on the European scene was minimal before war broke out, and the suspect and outcast Churchill.' But in 1963 Munby found it 'less easy to be pessimistic about the inherent possibilities of our society, however much we may detest the complacency and vulgarity of the Macmillan era in decline'. 'We are settling down to a secular society', he announced, 'to which the Church seems to be acclimatizing itself as it has acclimatized itself to most previous forms of society.' In this society, there is an explicit refusal 'to commit itself as a whole to any particular view of the nature of the universe and the place of man in it'; there are tensions between many groups as 'part of life' and homogeneity is recognized as unattainable; there is tolerance, 'giving every benefit of doubt to the varied expression of belief'; there are some common aims, but these are limited, and the main aim of a society with a modern economic system is 'to increase the goods and services available to people'; in decision-making there is an emphasis on the objective study of facts; and there are no official common images apart from 'one so vacuous and tawdry as the Royal Family'. Within such a society, Munby argued, the Christian Church can get on with its own 'specialized' job, which is to proclaim the truth about God and man by 'what goes on in church and what is tied up with it'; and Christians can be inspired by the Church to serve God and man humbly in the world as it actually exists, alongside many non-Christian collaborators. So many specialisms are needed that 'Mr Eliot's preference for "a common background of knowledge" can be taken as both impractical and undesirable.' Instead of Eliot's stress on Christian education and on an élite of teachers and pastors, Munby would have closed down 'an antiquated system of church schools' and opened 'centres where ordinary people can discuss their everyday problems'.

In assessing Munby's Christian defence of a secular society, we need not be too much concerned with the elements of complacency and vulgarity which marked his thought, just as elements of despair and élitism marked Eliot's thought. In the early 1960s the economic foundations of the liberal Western countries looked a great deal more secure than any intelligent person could reckon in the late 1970s. Moreover, the preoccupation with economic growth and affluence, although proper in one who was a professional economist as Munby was, may look vacuous and tawdry in comparison with Eliot's insights into the spiritual problems of an industrial civilization.

These, however, are defects in *The Idea of a Secular Society* which should in justice be ascribed to the necessary limitations of a man's time and temperament, and they are no more decisive than are the opposite defects in *The Idea of a Christian Society*. The real question is whether there has been any validity in Eliot's plea for a 'positive culture' more Christian in its content than was the general culture of England in the 1930s. Was Eliot wrong to regret that England was becoming 'pagan' or 'secular' as well as pluralist?

It is incontrovertible that England was more positively pluralist than Eliot acknowledged in 1939, and has become, over forty and more years, more pluralist than he in the 1930s admitted was possible in a society which would 'work'.[13] 'It is my contention

---

[13] See Alan D. Gilbert, *The Making of Post-Christian Britain* (London: Longman, 1980).

that we have today a culture which is mainly negative, but which, so far as it is positive, is still Christian.' So he stated near the beginning of *The Idea of a Christian Society*. It was a sweeping and false contention, failing to take into account the positive militancy of the secular world-view expounded by very influential figures such as H. G. Wells or Bertrand Russell. It also failed to reckon with the presence in the nation of a patriotic idealism, to be evoked by Churchill as he led Britain towards victory and by Attlee as he led it into the Welfare State. But the last paragraph of *The Idea of a Christian Society* sufficiently explains Eliot's apocalyptic mood. There the surrender to Hitler's claims in Czechoslovakia, purchasing as was hoped 'peace in our time', in September 1938, is said to have led to 'doubt of the validity of a civilization. We could not match conviction with conviction, we had no ideas with which we could either meet or oppose the ideas opposed to us. Was our society ... assembled around anything more permanent than a congeries of banks, insurance companies and industries ...?' Lecturing in March 1939, when 'the possibility of war was always present to my mind', Eliot had been further depressed by the fatuities of Moral Rearmament, a movement which had received some ecclesiastical blessings.

It is not surprising that in this crisis he turned with relief to the companionship of Christians such as J. H. Oldham, whose fine letter to *The Times* in October 1938 he reprinted in the published version of the lectures. Oldham (a layman) had made his name as a secretary of the International Missionary Council and in particular as the chief organizer of the ecumenical conference at Oxford in 1937 on 'Church, Community and State'. Eliot was one of a galaxy of distinguished thinkers who addressed that conference; he spoke on the real but limited importance of those differences between Christians which were based on nation, race and class.[14] Oldham impressed Eliot, as he impressed many other people of exceptional calibre, as a man who combined holiness with a shrewd grasp of current affairs. He had a flair for persuading busy leaders to give of their best, partly because he

[14] J. H. Oldham (ed.), *The Churches Survey Their Task* (London: Allen & Unwin, 1939), pp. 33–4.

took endless trouble to know precisely where they could contribute most usefully and partly perhaps because he made them speak clearly by being himself hard of hearing. Those whom Oldham drew together in this way were, in addition to those already assembled around 'Christendom' and the *New English Weekly*, the 'certain friends whose minds are engrossed by these and similar problems' mentioned in Eliot's 1939 Preface. They were engrossed by desperately serious problems during a world crisis—and they possessed acute and well-stocked minds.

That explains the mood in which Eliot lectured in 1939. If we try to sum up what has happened in England since then, we have to record a good deal of positive unity together with a large dose of what Eliot called negative liberalism. England has been composed of groups with very different basic convictions and the deepening economic troubles have encouraged social and political divisions, but these groups have had enough in common, and have derived enough satisfaction from their life together, for there to have been so far a stable—perhaps an excessive—pride in the English way of life, often expressed in an acceptance of the centralization of political authority in a deeply divided House of Commons. Positively, the attempts to stir up racial hatred or to deny equal opportunities to women have been made illegal. In this situation, however, the only democratic course is for the State to remain neutral over many religious and moral questions—and for the schools and broadcasting authorities for which the State legislates to emphasize the provision of information about religion rather than to embark on any major attempt to evangelize. Pluralism, not 'the Christian society', has turned out to be for most of the English the adequate foundation on which sufficient national unity and strength can be built. Presumably had Eliot lived to review his sociological writings he would have considered these developments, which he had not expected in the months between the surrender at Munich and the outbreak of the Second World War.

Yet his failure to predict the developments of the next forty years does not completely invalidate the plea which was the central burden of *The Idea of a Christian Society*. For his primary concern was with the unconscious unity of the English national culture and with the religious consciousness of the leaders of thought; and at this level which he wished to probe, the spiritual history of the twentieth century has not been very different from the story he told.

In the depths of English life ever since the catastrophic outbreak of the First World War there has been a negative note, although it has varied in intensity from period to period. There has been a failure of nerve when viewing the nation's long-term prospects, despite the military victories and the greater personal prosperity; a rejection of the cohesion of the traditional family together with a lack of confident ambition for the cities and large towns housing the majority of the population; and a lack of faith in the ability of the individual to master the challenges of private life, caused partly by the decline of the influence of traditional religion. (All this has been compatible with the dogged patriotism, since the feeling has been that other nations would sooner or later fall prey to the same anxieties.) All these attitudes received some of their classic modern expressions in the poetry and criticism of Eliot. He used to protest that *The Waste Land* and other melancholic poems written before his Christian conversion and baptism were not 'about' the society around him at that time, and it is true that before 1927 England was still in many ways Victorian. But his personal experiences enabled him to indicate distresses which were already not uncommon and which were to become after 1927 increasingly characteristic of the modern world: alienation from parents and their faith; rootlessness as a wanderer between nations and as an educated person without congenial employment; loneliness in the commercial and industrial city; disgust at the triviality and materialism of the privileged; disillusionment with the casual sex now easier than ever before; the deep wound of the failure of a marriage. That is why countless people have memorized lines of Eliot as cries of their own inner despair.

In a long journey which is as yet only partially recorded in print, he moved out of the academic security which he had tasted, and out of the hope that the detached pursuit of literature could be a substitute for the religion he had renounced in the Unitarian form of his boyhood, and out of the waste land, into 'the heart of light, the silence'. Soon after his baptism he explained to Paul Elmer More (another convert from Harvard humanism) that 'only Christianity helps to reconcile one to life which is otherwise disgusting.' In 1931 he wrote at length and with a penetrating sympathy about Pascal's *Pensées*. But he could give reasons of the mind for his religion; indeed, he insisted on them rather than on 'subjectivism' or the 'Inner Voice', and one of his themes became the celebration of the intellectual power of the Christian tradition. All that anguish, and the long answer of faith which brought a simplicity at the price of 'not less than everything', lay behind his insistence on the supreme importance of the individual's apprehension of the truth of Christian doctrine and of the glory of Christian behaviour.[15]

Having adopted this view of life where secularism was ultimately 'the horror, the horror', where man's greatest danger was alienation from God, where life before death was in the last analysis either hell or purgatory, Eliot inevitably considered that the most important function which a society could perform was to assist, rather than hinder, the soul's response to the Creator. Nevill Coghill was right to see that Eliot's 'governing idea' for a long time after his conversion was 'rebirth into supernatural life through a cycle of which the descent into the dark night of the soul is a recurring preliminary.'[16] Everything apart from the 'cold coming' of the Magi to a birth which was also a death was an escape from reality. Everyone who did not go on that pilgrimage remained hollow and 'they all go into the dark', since worldly life was Sweeney's 'birth and copulation, and death'. Pressing on to the Resurrection was what mattered, as for St Paul and for 'Marina' in 1930:

[15] There is no full biography, but see J. D. Margolis, *T. S. Eliot's Intellectual Development 1922–39* (Chicago: Chicago University Press, 1971), and Lyndall Gordon, *Eliot's Early Years* (Oxford: OUP, 1977).

[16] Richard Marsh and Tambimuttu (eds.), *T. S. Eliot: A Symposium* (London: Editions Poetry, 1948), p. 84.

Those who sharpen the tooth of the dog, meaning
Death
Those who glitter with the glory of the hummingbird,
meaning
Death
Those who sit in the stye of contentment, meaning
Death
Those who suffer the ecstasy of animals, meaning
Death

    Are become unsubstantial, reduced by a wind,
A breath of pine, and the woodsong fog,
By this grace dissolved in place ...

It seems that towards the end of his life, when he was very
happily married and very widely honoured, and when thirty
years of Christian self-discipline had brought him nearer to the
joy of the saints, Eliot might have assessed the human situation in
terms happier than those to be found in his poetry (or in his plays
before the end of *The Elder Statesman*). But we are assured by
those close to him that even in that rose garden he never
renounced his vision of the Christian life as being born again
through suffering, of the best rose as being also fire. He showed
as much in his booklet on George Herbert (1962). He did not
expect everyone to be as isolated, anguished or articulate as he
had been; indeed, already at the end of 1930s he said frankly that
'for the great mass of humanity' Christianity might be 'almost
wholly realized in behaviour' which seemed natural to them,
since 'their capacity for *thinking* about the objects of faith is
small.' But he then made plain his desire to see a society where
the religious decisions of thoughtful individuals would not be
handicapped, discouraged and mocked as his own had been and
where, for the people, 'the difficulty of behaving as Christians
should not impose an intolerable strain.' He wanted a society
where there would be 'a *respect* for the religious life, for the life of
prayer and contemplation'. And he believed that his fellow-
Christians ought to share his longing for such a society, so

different from the world which he and they had known. His own conversion had bewildered most of his clever friends, whose psychological explanations of the move had no doubt reached but not delighted his ears. In an essay of 1935 on 'Religion and Literature', he wrote that in England the period in which 'we are living' was a period in which 'nearly all contemporary novelists ... have never heard the Christian Faith spoken of as anything but an anachronism.' In a less well-known essay deploring 'Religion without Humanism' contributed to *Humanism and America*, edited by Norman Foerster (1930), he recalled of America: 'All the religious forms which have some ancestry, and many which have none, flourish there; but among persons whom I have known, there is hardly one who had any connection (not to say conviction) with any of them.'

If the need to make the sanctification of souls a little less difficult was Eliot's essential concern in his social criticism, he is surely entitled to the sympathy of anyone who appreciates the timeless importance of the religous quest. In particular he deserves the sympathy of other Christians. Fifty years after the publication of *The Waste Land*, lectures were given in the University of York which ended with a poet, Donald Davie, referring to 'the animus against Christianity as a hypocritical cheat which I find so common, so all but universal, among my friends and contemporaries'.[17] The devotion and vitality to be found in the churches are real—but so are the dangers to the future of Christianity in what seems to be a firmly non-Christian society. For those who have been converted to Christianity, and who want their fellows to have their same experience in their own ways, the confinement of the Church to an apparently small, archaic and dwindling ghetto, where it is a minority tolerated but isolated from the interests of the society as a whole, cannot be ideal or acceptable. For those who believe that Christianity provides the most important clues to our hard and mysterious lives, and that it has therefore been appropriate as the central thread in European and American civilization, the 'all but

[17] *'The Waste Land' in Different Voices*, A. D. Moody (ed.), (London: Edward Arnold, 1974), p. 234.

universal' dismissal of all traditional religion as the opium of the people, or as primitive magic, or as the emotional self-indulgence of neurotics, is the refusal of light in humanity's darkness. Reacting against these trends in English society at every level from those who read Marx, Fraser or Freud to those who read the picture-papers, Eliot defiantly announced (in a 1937 broadcast appended to *The Idea of a Christian Society*) that the Church 'wants everybody, and it wants each individual as a whole', so that 'it must struggle for a condition of society which will give the maximum of opportunity for us to lead wholly Christian lives, and the maximum of opportunity for others to become Christians.' He reacted so strongly because he valued so highly what he had found in Christianity—a discovery which he indicated, in a few sentences pregnant with self-revelation, in his contribution to *Humanism and America*:

On the following point I speak with diffidence, recognizing my lack of qualification where qualification is severe and exact. Humanism has much to say of Discipline and Order and Control; and I have parroted these terms myself. I found no discipline in humanism; only a little intellectual discipline from a little study of philosophy. But the difficult discipline is the discipline and training of emotion; this the modern world has great need of; so great need that it hardly understands what the word means; and this I have found is only attainable through dogmatic religion. I do not say that dogmatic religion is justified because it supplies this need—that is just the psychologism and the anthropocentrism that I wish to avoid—but merely state my belief that in no other way can the need be supplied. There is much chatter about mysticism: for the modern world the word means some spattering indulgence of emotion, instead of the most terrible concentration and askesis. But it takes perhaps a lifetime merely to realize that men like the forest sages, and the desert sages, and finally the Victorines and John of the Cross and (in his fashion) Ignatius really *mean what they say*. Only those have the right to talk of discipline who have looked into the Abyss. The need of the modern world is the discipline and training of the emotions; which neither the intellectual training of philosophy or science, nor the wisdom of humanism, nor the negative instruction of psychology can give.

To this reprint of *The Idea of a Christian Society* some other social writings have been added. For many years they have been accessible only with difficulty and this fact may help to explain why such a distorted picture of Eliot as a social thinker appears to have gained acceptance.

First comes the review of *The Idea of a Christian Society* which Eliot evidently thought the most important; he wrote an article and also a public letter in reply to it, and these are now added. Maurice Reckitt's review in the *New English Weekly* on 7 December 1939 shows that the book was not 'received with incomprehension' (as was the almost simultaneous *Family Reunion* according to its director, E. Martin Browne). It was discussed widely and favourably in the press, and this review picks out the points which seemed most important at the time to another Christian thinker of distinction. It continues the discussion by raising a point which, as Eliot generously commented, 'greatly transcends in importance the book itself'. Is it sufficiently Christian to want a society 'in which the natural end of man—virtue and well-being in community—is acknowledged for all, and the supernatural end—beatitude—for those who have eyes to see it'? Is it enough to expect most people in that society to be 'not individually better than they are now' except that they would express their membership of the Christian society by some 'behaviour and conformity'? In an article called 'A Sub-Pagan Society?' Eliot replied that his idea was based on St Thomas Aquinas, except that 'my City must find a place for inhabitants who fail to recognize the Christian revelation.' Christendom, he recalled, has never lived up to the standards of the New Testament, because it always has been 'a human society . . . liable always and at any moment to fall out of the hand of God'. In a subsequent letter to the editor he admits that his phrasing had not made clear his intention, which had been 'to limit myself to the *minimal* requirements in society before it could be *called* a Christian society'.

The next two writings show him clarifying some of the ideas in his 1939 lectures and communicating them to a wider public. 'Towards a Christian Britain' was broadcast by the BBC on 10 April 1941. 'Christian and Natural Virtues' was printed as part of the *Christian News-Letter* of 3 September 1941. It is of special interest because of what it says about patriotism.

Next comes the *Christian News-Letter* of 21 August 1940. The title 'Freedom in Wartime' has been added because the essay shows Eliot wrestling with the practical problems of the rights of conscientious objectors to military service, and of foreign internees, at the height of the Nazi threat to Britain's freedom. Such a document, written at such a time, disposes of the allegations that his political philosophy was totalitarian, inhumane or purely theoretical. Similarly, this reprint of the *Christian News-Letter* of 28 August 1940 has been given the new title 'The Diversity of French Opinion' and shows how ignorant is any accusation that Eliot's sympathy was confined to the extreme Right in French politics. The shorter essay which follows, on 'The Christian Education of France', comes from the *Christian News-Letter* of 3 September 1941 and helps to rebut any description of Eliot as an anti-Semite or as an advocate of reactionary excesses. His love of France shines out in these pieces, written in that nation's darkest hour.

The next essays, which will also come as a surprise to some who have written off Eliot as hopelessly reactionary, consider education in a Christian society. The *Christian News-Letter* of 13 March 1940 reminds readers of the importance of the values of wisdom and holiness, of which 'education for culture' and 'character-building' are 'the atrophied vestiges'. But he also assures them that he is 'not anxious to scrap anything' such as laboratories or technical schools and that 'there is no system to which we can go back.' As education is reconstructed he simply wants to ask some fundamental questions, such as these: what is the type of man which a society holds in highest honour, ought everyone to stay at school until the age of eighteen, must the provision of equal opportunities to young people result in so much social mobility that education produces 'a race of spiritual nomads'?

Another essay, now reprinted from *The Life of the Church and the Order of Society* (1942), was presented as a paper to the conference which Archbishop William Temple summoned to Malvern College for three days in January 1941. The meeting was intended 'to consider from the Anglican point of view what are the fundamental facts which are directly relevant to the ordering of the new society which is quite evidently emerging, and how Christian thought can be shaped to play a leading part in the reconstruction after the war is over'. Four hundred bishops, clergy or laity gathered and were, on the whole, bemused by the papers, which were too many, too long and too full of jargon. Such discussion as took place mainly concerned the challenges of Socialism and Pacifism, not Eliot's subjects. But his paper to this audience deserves to be studied alongside the lecture on 'The Issue of Religion' in a course on 'The Aims of Education' delivered at Chicago in 1950–51 and published in *To Criticize the Critic*.

In 1941 Eliot urged that 'no adequate conception of education is possible without the leadership of the Church.' Drawing mainly on American experiences, he traced the rise of specialization in the schools and the universities, the rise of humanism with its opposed ideals of unity and wisdom, and the rise of a Christian concern to give young people what humanism could not supply. 'The Christian interest cannot ask less than that every Christian child should be trained to *understand* his faith to the extent of his capacities—an expectation which is very far from being realized today.' Eliot took care to dissociate himself from the 'public school' or 'gentleman' tradition founded by Thomas Arnold as Headmaster of Rugby (although he was lecturing in a public school and his chairman, Archbishop Temple, had been a boy at Rugby and had entered life as a disciple of Arnold's). 'The Christian doctrine of Arnold', he observed, 'was one which would be vague, unsound and perhaps heretical at any time'—and was also irrelevant in that it 'assumed

35

that the nation was Christian'. At the same time he took care not to advocate handing over educational control to the Church, since 'we ought to aim to avoid, not promote, centralization and standardization.' But he pleaded that 'the soul of education' should be inspired by Christianity rather than by 'such wordliness as will make the more limited efforts of religious teaching to be in vain'—a plea which few experts on religious education in the 1980s would think ridiculously dated.

A paper 'On the Place and Function of the Clerisy' was written for discussion at the meeting of the Moot in December 1944. It is reprinted here although it was made public by Roger Kojecky in 1971, because it bridged the gap between *The Idea of a Christian Society* and *Notes towards the Definition of Culture*. It tried to think out the composition and function of the 'clerisy'. This was Coleridge's term for the 'clerical élite' of his day, but not only clergymen were included by Coleridge or by Eliot. The 'clerisy' here described is wider than anything Coleridge envisaged, and wider than the 'Community of Christians' desired in Eliot's own 1939 lectures (it embraces Noël Coward), but the Community of Christians would certainly have been 'clerical' in the sense here analysed.

This volume concludes with a reprint of Eliot's essay on 'Revelation' from the symposium with that title edited by John Baillie and Hugh Martin and published at Eliot's behest by Faber and Faber in 1937. It is a more defensible account of the 1930s than the one which he adopted after the shock of the 1938 surrender to Hitler, and it is the fullest statement which he made in prose of his religious position when he had sobered down after his conversion.

After a preliminary consideration of the secular world-view as popularized by, for example, H. G. Wells, Eliot noted that 'the more reflective writers of this generation—those whose attention is not wholly taken up by prospective political and social reforms, and who therefore have time to consider final ends—feel the need for assuring us that mankind still has something to live for.' After brushing aside Bertrand Russell's 'conquest of happiness', he suggested that a conversion to Communism or 'Marxist mysticism' might include 'a desire to satisfy repressed Christian impulses without embracing Christianity', adducing the case of André Gide. He paid more attention to the Buddhist alternative, particularly since Irving Babbitt, with whom so much of his own intellectual life had been a dialogue since the classroom at Harvard in 1909–10, appeared to have embraced it in an essay published in 1936. This passage is of special interest because Eliot reported (for example, he told Stephen Spender) that at the time of *The Waste Land* he had himself seriously considered becoming a Buddhist (so that the 'Fire Sermon' on London life had that existential significance). The humanist Babbitt's admiration of the Buddhist's 'quality of will' is also of interest in view of the prestige enjoyed by Eastern wisdom in the disillusioned West during the 1960s and 1970s. But Eliot protested that Babbitt had invalidated his praises of Buddhism at the expense of Christianity by a failure to understand the Christian mystical tradition and by an insistence on identifying Christianity with 'some of the decayed forms of religiosity that he had seen about him', while glossing over the fact that a belief in reincarnation was essential to Buddhism. These are comments which Christians might have been expected to make more loudly than they did when the dialogue of mankind's great faiths reopened in the 1960s.

Eliot then turned to 'the psychological mysticism that is a phenomenon of decadence rather than of growth'—a phenomenon of the 1930s, advocated by Aldous Huxley, that had 'something in common with the Buddhism of Irving Babbitt'. It had much more in common with the hairy Age of Aquarius, and with the arrival of 'flower power', celebrated by hippies and other Orientalizing radicals in the 1960s and later. Long before the Age of Aquarius Eliot observed that 'peace . . . cannot be an ultimate good cause.' It is 'not an end but a means', and the advocacy of meditation in order to strengthen the Will to Peace still leaves unanswered the theological question: what is the chief end of man? The same question remained, he thought, after D. H. Lawrence's 'lifelong search for a religion'. For Lawrence the modern world of enlightenment and progress was a nightmare, but instead of turning to Huxley's high-minded mysticism 'he wished to go as low as possible in the scale of human consciousness, in order to find something that he could assure himself was *real*.' Eliot's response is of interest in view of the phallic cult which flourished openly in England after the failure of the attempt to prosecute the publishers of *Lady Chatterley's Lover* in 1960. Eliot (a lifelong opponent of the censorship of works of literary merit) was willing to appear for the defence in that symbolic trial. But in 1937, as later, he expressed shrewd reservations about that novel and assessed Lawrence's sex-centred religion as magic, as a 'fundamentally chimerical' attempt both to worship nature and to manipulate it. This contrast between Huxley's psychological mysticism and Lawrence's magic of the body led Eliot into a concluding assessment of 'the principal characteristics of philosophies without revelation'. They are unstable, reappearing again and again and evoking each other's excesses, but they are seductive, always appearing as new and as capable of setting things right at once. Their appeal is symptomatic of the effects of the repression of the religious sentiment in an age when 'the whole tendency of education . . . has been for a very long time to form minds more and more adapted to secularism.'

Such was Eliot's basic analysis of the spiritual condition of the country which in 1938 seemed to lack convictions to match Hitler's. It might seem that his analysis was falsified by wartime phenomena such as the National Days of Prayer, the circulation of the *Christian News-Letter* (over 9000 a week by 1940), the influence of William Temple or the welcome to his own *Four Quartets*. But at least in some moods he wondered whether the power or afterglow of Christianity was not all the time decreasing. In an address delivered in 1943 and subsequently developed for delivery to an audience in Paris in 1945, he declared: 'The trouble of the modern age is not merely the inability to believe certain things about God and man which our forefathers believed, but the inability to *feel* towards God and man as they did. A belief in which you no longer believe is something which to some extent you can still understand; but when religious

38

feeling disappears, the words in which men have been glad to express it become meaningless.' It would follow that the term 'secular', which he had wished to avoid in his preference for 'pagan' or 'infidel', was becoming inescapable.[18]

Eliot's analysis of 1937, thus sombrely revised during the war, would have to be altered in many details if it were to be related to the figures dominating the cultural landscape twenty, thirty or forty years later, but even in our day it seems to be worth considering. Indeed, the study of Eliot's poetry at school and university has become one of the most potent ways of keeping alive the religious and moral imagination in the English-speaking world in the 1980s. At the end of his study of *Eliot and His Age*,[19] the American scholar Russell Kirk quoted words which Eliot wrote about F. H. Bradley. 'We fight for lost causes because we know that our defeat and dismay may be the preface to our successors' victory, though that victory itself will be temporary; we fight rather to keep something alive than in the expectation that anything will triumph.' Holding that the cause to which Eliot was converted was essentially the cause of truth, even during the 1980s some feel that the words inscribed on his memorial in Poets' Corner in Westminster Abbey apply to the heart of his social criticism:

> ... the communication
> Of the dead is tongued with fire beyond the language of the
> living.

The Deanery   DAVID L. EDWARDS
Norwich   *1982*

---

[18] More recent discussion by professional sociologists, more finely nuanced than Eliot's, has included David Martin, *The Religious and the Secular* (London: Routledge, 1969), and *The Dilemmas of Contemporary Religion* (Oxford: Blackwell, 1978). In *Religion in Secular Society* (London: Watts, 1966), another distinguished sociologist, Bryan Wilson, accepted a profound secularization as irreversible, and in *Religion in Sociological Perspective* (Oxford: OUP, 1982) he lamented many of its results.

[19] Russell Kirk, *Eliot and His Age* (New York: Random House, 1971).

The Idea of a
Christian Society

PREFACE

THE three lectures which, with some revision and division, are here printed, were delivered in March 1939 at the invitation of the Master and Fellows of Corpus Christi College, Cambridge, on the Boutwood Foundation. I wish to express my thanks to the Master and Fellows for this honour and privilege. The notes I have added while preparing the lectures for press.

My point of departure has been the suspicion that the current terms in which we discuss international affairs and political theory may only tend to conceal from us the real issues of contemporary civilization. As I have chosen to consider such a large problem, it should be obvious that the following pages can have but little importance by themselves, and that they can only be of use if taken as an individual contribution to a discussion which must occupy many minds for a long time to come. To aim at originality would be an impertinence: at most, this essay can be only an original arrangement of ideas which did not belong to me before and which must become the property of whoever can use them. I owe a great deal to conversations with certain friends whose minds are engrossed by these and similar problems: to make specific acknowledgement might have the effect of imputing to these friends an inconvenient responsibility for my own faults of reasoning. But I owe a great deal also to a number of recent books: for instance, to Mr Christopher Dawson's *Beyond Politics*, to Mr Middleton Murry's *The Price of Leadership*, and to writings of the Rev. V. A. Demant (whose *Religious Prospect* has appeared too recently for me to have made use of it). And I am deeply indebted to the works of Jacques Maritain, especially his *Humanisme intégral*.

I trust that the reader will understand from the beginning that this book does not make any plea for a 'religious revival' in a sense with which we are already familiar. That is a task for which I am incompetent, and the term seems to me to imply a possible separation of religious feeling from religious thinking which I do not accept—or which I do not find acceptable for our present difficulties. An anonymous writer has recently observed in *The New English Weekly* (13 July 1939) that

> men have lived by spiritual institutions (of some kind) in every society, and also by political institutions and, indubitably, by economic activities. Admittedly, they have, at different periods, tended to put their trust mainly in one of the three as the real cement of society, but at no time have they wholly excluded the others, because it is impossible to do so.

This is an important, and in its context valuable, distinction; but it should be clear that what I am concerned with here is not spiritual institutions in their separated aspect, but the organization of values, and a direction of religious thought which must inevitably proceed to a criticism of political and economic systems.

1

The fact that a problem will certainly take a long time to solve, and that it will demand the attention of many minds for several generations, is no justification for postponing the study. And, in times of emergency, it may prove in the long run that the problems we have postponed or ignored, rather than those we have failed to attack successfully, will return to plague us. Our difficulties of the moment must always be dealt with somehow: but our permanent difficulties are difficulties of every moment. The subject with which I am concerned in the following pages is one to which I am convinced we ought to turn our attention now, if we hope ever to be relieved of the immediate perplexities that fill our minds. It is urgent because it is fundamental; and its urgency is the reason for a person like myself attempting to address, on a subject beyond his usual scope, that public which is likely to read what he writes on other subjects. This is a subject which I could, no doubt, handle much better were I a profound scholar in any of several fields. But I am not writing for scholars, but for people like myself; some defects may be compensated by some advantages; and what one must be judged by, scholar or no, is not particularized knowledge but one's total harvest of thinking, feeling, living and observing human beings.

While the practice of poetry need not in itself confer wisdom or accumulate knowledge, it ought at least to train the mind in one habit of universal value: that of analysing the meanings of words: of those that one employs oneself, as well as the words of others. In using the term 'Idea' of a Christian Society I do not mean primarily a concept derived from the study of any societies which we may choose to call Christian; I mean something that can only be found in an understanding of the end to which a Christian Society, to deserve the name, must be directed. I do not limit the application of the term to a perfected Christian Society on earth; and I do not comprehend in it societies merely because some profession of Christian faith, or some vestige of Christian practice, is retained. My concern with contemporary society, accordingly, will not be primarily with specific defects, abuses or injustices but with the question. vhat—if any—is the 'idea' of the society in which we live: to what end is it arranged?

The Idea of a Christian Society is one which we can accept or reject; but if we are to accept it, we must treat Christianity with a great deal more *intellectual* respect than is our wont; we must treat it as being for the individual a matter primarily of thought and not of feeling. The consequences of such an attitude are too serious to be acceptable to everybody: for when the Christian faith is not only felt, but thought, it has practical results which may be inconvenient. For to see the Christian faith in this way—and to see it in this way is not necessarily to accept it, but only to understand the real issues—is to see that the difference between the Idea of a Neutral Society (which is that of the society in which we live at present) and the Idea of a Pagan Society (such as the upholders of democracy abominate) is, in the long run, of minor importance. I am not at this moment concerned with the means for bringing a Christian Society into existence; I am not even primarily concerned with making it appear desirable; but I am very much concerned with making clear its difference from the kind of society in which we are now living. Now, to understand the society in which he lives, must be to the interest of every conscious thinking person. The current terms in which we describe our society, the contrasts with other societies by which we—of the 'Western Democracies'—eulogize it, only operate to deceive and stupefy us. To speak of ourselves as a Christian Society, in contrast to that of Germany or Russia, is an abuse of terms. We mean only that we have a society in which no one is penalized for the *formal profession* of Christianity; but we conceal from ourselves the unpleasant knowledge of the real values by which we live. We conceal from ourselves, moreover, the similarity of our society to those which we execrate: for we should have to admit, if we recognized the similarity, that the foreigners do better. I suspect that in our loathing of totalitarianism, there is infused a good deal of admiration for its efficiency.

The political philosopher of the present time, even when he is a Christian himself, is not usually concerned with the possible structure of a Christian state. He is occupied with the possibility of a just State in general, and when he is not an adherent of one or another secular system, is inclined to accept our present system as one to be improved, but not fundamentally altered. Theological writers have more to say that is relevant to my subject. I am not alluding to those writers who endeavour to infuse a vague, and sometimes debased, Christian spirit into the ordinary conduct of affairs; or to those who endeavour, at moments of emergency, to apply Christian principles to particular political situations. Relevant to my subject are the writings of the Christian sociologists—those writers who criticize our economic system in the light of Christian ethics. Their work consists in proclaiming in general, and demonstrating in particular, the incompatibility of Christian principle and a great deal of our social practice. They appeal to the spirit of justice and humanity with which most of us profess to be inspired; they appeal also to the practical reason, by demonstrating that much in our system is not only iniquitous, but in the long run unworkable and conducive to disaster. Many of the changes which such writers advocate, while deducible from Christian principles, can recommend themselves to any intelligent and disinterested person, and do not require a Christian society to carry them into effect, or Christian belief to render them acceptable: though they are changes which would make it more possible for the individual Christian to live out his Christianity. I am here concerned only secondarily with the changes in economic organization, and only secondarily with the life of the devout Christian: my primary interest is a change in our social attitude, such a change only as could bring about anything worthy to be called a Christian Society. That such a change would compel changes in our organization of industry and commerce and financial credit, that it would facilitate, where it now impedes, the life of devotion for those who are capable of it, I feel certain. But my point of departure is different from that of the sociologists and economists; though I depend upon them for enlightenment, and a test of my Christian Society would be that it should bring about such reforms as they propose; and though the kind of 'change of spirit' which can testify for itself by nothing better than a new revivalistic vocabulary, is a danger against which we must be always on guard.

My subject touches also upon that of another class of Christian writer: that of the ecclesiastical controversialists. The subject of Church and State is, again, not my primary concern. It is not, except at moments which lend themselves to newspaper exploitation, a subject in which the general public takes much interest; and at the moments when the public's interest is aroused, the public is never well enough informed to have the right to an opinion. My subject is a preliminary to the problem of Church and State: it involves that problem in its widest terms and in its most general interest. A usual attitude is to take for granted the existing State, and ask: 'What Church?' But before we consider what should be the relation of Church and State, we should first ask: 'What State?' Is there any sense in which we can speak of a 'Christian State', any sense in which the State can be regarded as Christian? For even if the nature of the State be such, that we cannot speak of it in its Idea as either Christian or non-Christian, yet is it obvious that Actual States may vary to such an extent that the relation of the Church to the State may be anything from overt hostility to a more or less harmonious cooperation of different institutions in the same society. What I mean by the Christian State is not any particular political form, but whatever State is suitable to a Christian Society, whatever State a particular Christian Society develops for itself. Many Christians there are, I know, who do not believe that a Church in relation to the State is necessary for a Christian Society; and I shall have to give reasons, in later pages, for believing that it is. The point to be made at this stage is that neither the classical English treatises on Church and State, nor contemporary discussion of the subject, give me the assistance that I need. For the earlier treatises, and indeed all up to the present time, assume the existence of a Christian Society; modern writers sometime assume that what we have is a pagan society: and it is just these assumptions that I wish to question.

Your opinion of what can be done for this country in the future, and incidentally your opinion of what ought to be the relations of Church and State, will depend upon the view you take of the contemporary situation. We can abstract three positive historical points: that at which Christians are a new minority in a society of positive pagan traditions—a position which cannot recur within any future with which we are concerned; the point at which the whole society can be called Christian, whether in one body or in a prior or subsequent stage of division into sects; and finally the point at which practising Christians must be recognized as a minority (whether static or diminishing) in a society which has ceased to be Christian. Have we reached the third point? Different observers will give different reports; but I would remark that there are two points of view for two contexts. The first is that a society has ceased to be Christian when religious practices have been abandoned, when behaviour ceases to be regulated by reference to Christian principle, and when in effect prosperity in this world for the individual or for the group has become the sole conscious aim. The other point of view, which is less readily apprehended, is that a society has not ceased to be Christian until it has become positively something else. It is my contention that we have today a culture which is mainly negative, but which, so far as it is positive, is still Christian. I do not think that it can remain negative, because a negative culture has ceased to be efficient in a world where economic as well as spiritual forces are proving the efficiency of cultures which, even when pagan, are positive; and I believe that the choice before us is between the formation of a new Christian culture, and the acceptance of a pagan one. Both involve radical changes; but I believe that the majority of us, if we could be faced immediately with all the changes which will only be accomplished in several generations, would prefer Christianity.

I do not expect everyone to agree that our present organization and temper of society—which proved, in its way, highly successful during the nineteenth century—is 'negative': many will maintain that British, French and American civilization still stands integrally for something positive. And there are others who will insist, that if our culture is negative, then a negative culture is the right thing to have. There are two distinct arguments to be employed in rebuttal: one, an argument of principle, that such a culture is undesirable; the other, a judgment of fact, that it must disappear anyway. The defenders of the present order fail to perceive either how far it is vestigial of a positive Christianity, or how far it has already advanced towards something else.

There is one class of persons to which one speaks with difficulty, and another to which one speaks in vain. The second, more numerous and obstinate than may at first appear, because it represents a state of mind into which we are all prone through natural sloth to relapse, consists of those people who cannot believe that things will ever be very different from what they are at the moment. From time to time, under the influence perhaps of some persuasive writer or speaker, they may have an instant of disquiet or hope; but an invincible sluggishness of imagination makes them go on behaving as if nothing would ever change. Those to whom one speaks with difficulty, but not perhaps in vain, are the persons who believe that great changes must come, but are not sure either of what is inevitable, or of what is probable, or of what is desirable.

What the Western world has stood for—and by that I mean the terms to which it has attributed sanctity—is 'Liberalism' and 'Democracy'. The two terms are not identical or inseparable. The term 'Liberalism' is the more obviously ambiguous, and is now less in favour; but the term 'Democracy' is at the height of its popularity. When a term has become so universally sanctified as 'democracy' now is, I begin to wonder whether it means anything, in meaning too many things: it has arrived perhaps at the position of a Merovingian Emperor, and wherever it is invoked, one begins to look for the Major of the Palace. Some persons have gone so far as to affirm, as something self-evident, that democracy is the only regime compatible with Christianity; on the other hand, the word is not abandoned by sympathizers with the government of Germany. If anybody ever attacked democracy, I might discover what the word meant. Certainly there is a sense in which Britain and America are more democratic than Germany; but on the other hand, defenders of the totalitarian system can make out a plausible case for maintaining that what we have is not democracy, but financial oligarchy.

Mr Christopher Dawson considers that 'what the non-dictatorial States stand for today is not Liberalism but Democracy', and goes on to foretell the advent in these States of a kind of totalitarian democracy. I agree with his prediction, but if one is considering, not merely the non-dictatorial States, but the societies to which they belong, his statement does less than justice to the extent to which Liberalism still permeates our minds and affects our attitude towards much of life. That Liberalism may be a tendency towards something very different from itself, is a possibility in its nature. For it is something which tends to release energy rather than accumulate it, to relax, rather than to fortify. It is a movement not so much defined by its end, as by its starting point; away from, rather than towards, something definite. Our point of departure is more real to us than our destination; and the destination is likely to present a very different picture when arrived at, from the vaguer image formed in imagination. By destroying traditional social habits of the people, by dissolving their natural collective consciousness into individual constituents, by licensing the opinions of the most foolish, by substituting instruction for education, by encouraging cleverness rather than wisdom, the upstart rather than the qualified, by fostering a notion of *getting on* to which the alternative is a hopeless apathy, Liberalism can prepare the way for that which is its own negation: the artificial, mechanized or brutalized control which is a desperate remedy for its chaos.

It must be evident that I am speaking of Liberalism in a sense much wider than any which can be fully exemplified by the history of any political party, and equally in a wider sense than any in which it has been used in ecclesiastical controversy. True, the tendency of Liberalism can be more clearly illustrated in religious history than in politics, where principle is more diluted by necessity, where observation is more confused by detail and distracted by reforms each valid within its own limited reference. In religion, Liberalism may be characterized as a progressive discarding of elements in historical Christianity which appear superfluous or obsolete, confounded with practices and abuses which are legitimate objects of attack. But as its movement is controlled rather by its origin than by any goal, it loses force after a series of rejections, and with nothing to destroy is left with nothing to uphold and with nowhere to go. With religious Liberalism, however, I am no more specifically concerned than with political Liberalism: I am concerned with a state of mind which, in certain circumstances, can become universal and infect opponents as well as defenders. And I shall have expressed myself very ill if I give the impression that I think of

Liberalism as something simply to be rejected and extirpated, as an evil for which there is a simple alternative. It is a necessary negative element; when I have said the worst of it, that worst comes only to this, that a negative element made to serve the purpose of a positive is objectionable. In the sense in which Liberalism is contrasted with Conservatism, both can be equally repellent: if the former can mean chaos, the latter can mean petrifaction. We are always faced both with the question 'what must be destroyed?' and with the question 'what must be preserved?' and neither Liberalism nor Conservatism, which are not philosophies and may be merely habits, is enough to guide us.

In the nineteenth century the Liberal Party had its own conservatism, and the Conservative Party had its own liberalism; neither had a political philosophy. To hold a political philosophy is in fact not the function of a political, that is, a Parliamentary party: a party with a political philosophy is a revolutionary party. The politics of political parties is not my concern. Nor am I concerned with the politics of a revolutionary party. If a revolutionary party attains its true end, its political philosophy will, by a process of growth, become that of a whole culture; if it attains its more facile end, its political philosophy will be that of a dominant class or group, in a society in which the majority will be passive, and the minority oppressed. But a political philosophy is not merely a formalized system set forth by a theorist. The permanent value of such treatises as Aristotle's *Politics* and *Poetics* is found at the opposite extreme to anything that we can call *doctrinaire*. Just as his views on dramatic poetry were derived from a study of the existing works of Attic drama, so his political theory was founded on a perception of the unconscious aims implicit in Athenian democracy at its best. His limitations are the condition of his universality; and instead of ingenious theories spun out of his head, he wrote studies full of universal wisdom. Thus, what I mean by a political philosophy is not merely even the conscious formulation of the ideal aims of a people, but the substratum of collective temperament, ways of behaviour and unconscious values which provides the material for the formulation. What we are seeking is not a programme for a party, but a way of life for a people: it is this which totalitarianism has sought partly to revive, and partly to impose by force upon its peoples. Our choice now is not between one abstract form and another, but between a pagan, and necessarily stunted culture, and a religious, and necessarily imperfect culture.

The attitudes and beliefs of Liberalism are destined to disappear, are already disappearing. They belong to an age of free exploitation which has passed; and our danger now is, that the term may come to signify for us only the disorder the fruits of which we inherit, and not the permanent value of the negative element. Out of Liberalism itself come philosophies which deny it. We do not proceed, from Liberalism to its apparent end of authoritarian democracy, at a uniform pace in every respect. There are so many centres of it—Britain, France, America and the Dominions—that the development of western society must proceed more slowly than that of a compact body like Germany, and its tendencies are less apparent. Furthermore, those who are the most convinced of the necessity of *étatisme* as a control of some activities of life, can be the loudest professors of libertarianism in others, and insist upon the preserves of 'private life' in which each man may obey his own convictions or follow his own whim: while imperceptibly this domain of 'private life' becomes smaller and smaller, and may eventually disappear altogether. It is possible that a wave of terror of the consequences of depopulation might lead to legislation having the effect of compulsory breeding.

If, then, Liberalism disappears from the philosophy of life of a people, what positive is left? We are left only with the term 'democracy', a term which, for the present generation, still has a Liberal connotation of 'freedom'. But totalitarianism can retain the terms 'freedom' and 'democracy' and give them its own meaning: and its right to them is not so easily disproved as minds inflamed by passion suppose. We are in danger of finding ourselves with nothing to stand for except a *dislike* of everything maintained by Germany and/or Russia: a dislike which, being a compost of newspaper sensations and prejudice, can have two results, at the same time, which appear at first incompatible. It may lead us to reject possible improvements, because we should owe them to the example of one or both of these countries; and it may equally well lead us to be mere imitators *à rebours*, in making us adopt uncritically almost any attitude which a foreign nation rejects.

We are living at present in a kind of doldrums between opposing winds of doctrine, in a period in which one political philosophy has lost its cogency for behaviour, though it is still the only one in which public speech can be framed. This is very bad for the English language; it is this disorder (for which we are all to blame) and not individual insincerity, which is responsible for the hollowness of many political and ecclesiastical utterances. You have only to examine the mass of newspaper leading articles, the mass of political exhortation, to appreciate the fact that good prose cannot be written by a people without convictions. The fundamental objection to Fascist doctrine, the one which we conceal from ourselves because it might condemn ourselves as well, is that it is pagan. There are other objections too, in the political and economic sphere, but they are not objections that we can make with dignity until we set our own affairs in order. There are still other objections, to oppression and violence and cruelty, but however strongly we feel, these are objections to means and not to ends. It is true that we sometimes use the word 'pagan', and in the same context refer to ourselves as 'Christian'. But we always dodge the real issue. Our newspapers have done all they could with the red herring of the 'German national religion', an eccentricity which is after all no odder than some cults held in Anglo-Saxon countries: this 'German national religion' is comforting in that it persuades us that *we* have a Christian civilization; it helps to disguise the fact that our aims, like Germany's, are materialistic. And the last thing we should like to do would be to examine the 'Christianity' which, in such contexts as this, we say we keep.

If we have got so far as accepting the belief that the only alternative to a progressive and insidious adaptation to totalitarian worldliness for which the pace is already set, is to aim at a Christian society, we need to consider both what kind of a society we have at this time, and what a Christian society would be like. We should also be quite sure of what we want: if your real ideals are those of materialistic efficiency, then the sooner you know your own mind, and face the consequences, the better. Those who, either complacently or despairingly, suppose that the aim of Christianization is chimerical, I am not here attempting to convert. To those who realize what a well organized pagan society would mean for us, there is nothing to say. But it is as well to remember that the imposition of a pagan theory of the State does not necessarily mean a wholly pagan society. A compromise between the theory of the State and the tradition of society exists in Italy, a country which is still mainly agricultural and Catholic. The more highly industrialized the country, the more easily a materialistic philosophy will flourish in it, and the more deadly that philosophy will be. Britain has been highly industrialized longer than any other country. And the tendency of unlimited industrialism is to create bodies of men and women—of all classes—detached from tradition, alienated from religion, and susceptible to mass suggestion: in other words, a mob. And a mob will be no less a mob if it is well fed, well clothed, well housed, and well disciplined.

The Liberal notion that religion was a matter of private belief and of conduct in private life, and that there is no reason why Christians should not be able to accommodate themselves to any world which treats them good-naturedly, is becoming less and less tenable. This notion would seem to have become accepted gradually, as a false inference from the subdivision of English Christianity into sects, and the happy results of universal toleration. The reason why members of different communions have been able to rub along together, is that in the greater part of the ordinary business of life they have shared the same assumptions about behaviour. When they have been wrong, they have been wrong together. We have less excuse than our ancestors for un-Christian conduct, because the growth of an un-Christian society about us, its more obvious intrusion upon our lives, has been breaking down the comfortable distinction between public and private morality. The problem of leading a Christian life in a non-Christian society is now very present to us, and it is a very different problem from that of the accommodation between an Established Church and dissenters. It is not merely the problem of a minority in a society of *individuals* holding an alien belief. It is the problem constituted by our implication in a network of institutions from which we cannot dissociate ourselves: institutions the operation of which appears no longer neutral, but non-Christian. And as for the Christian who is not conscious of his dilemma—and he is in the majority—he is becoming more and more de-Christianized by all sorts of unconscious pressure: paganism holds all the most valuable advertising space. Anything like Christian traditions transmitted from generation to generation within the family must disappear, and the small body of Christians will consist entirely of adult recruits. I am saying nothing at this point that has not been said before by others, but it is relevant. I am not concerned with the problem of Christians as a persecuted minority. When the Christian is treated as an enemy of the State, his course is very much harder, but it is simpler. I am concerned with the dangers to the tolerated minority; and in the modern world, it may turn out that the most intolerable thing for Christians is to be tolerated.

To attempt to make the prospect of a Christian society immediately attractive to those who see no prospect of deriving direct personal benefit from it, would be idle; even the majority of professing Christians may shrink from it. No scheme for a change of society can be made to appear immediately palatable, except by falsehood, until society has become so desperate that it will accept any change. A Christian society only becomes acceptable after you have fairly examined the alternatives. We might, of course, merely sink into an apathetic decline: without faith, and therefore without faith in ourselves; without a philosophy of life, either Christian or pagan; and without art. Or we might get a 'totalitarian democracy', different but having much in common with other pagan societies, because we shall have changed step by step in order to keep pace with them: a state of affairs in which we shall have regimentation and conformity,

without respect for the needs of the individual soul; the puritan-
ism of a hygienic morality in the interest of efficiency; uniformity of opinion through propaganda, and art only encouraged
when it flatters the official doctrines of the time. To those who
can imagine, and are therefore repelled by, such a prospect, one
can assert that the only possibility of control and balance is a
religious control and balance; that the only hopeful course for a
society which would thrive and continue its creative activity in
the arts of civilization, is to become Christian. That prospect
involves, at least, discipline, inconvenience and discomfort: but
here as hereafter the alternative to hell is purgatory.

II

My thesis has been, simply, that a liberalized or negative condition of society must either proceed into a gradual decline of
which we can see no end, or (whether as a result of catastrophe or
not) reform itself into a positive shape which is likely to be
effectively secular. We need not assume that this secularism will
approximate closely to any system in the past or to any that can
now be observed in order to be apprehensive about it: the
Anglo-Saxons display a capacity for *diluting* their religion, probably in excess of that of any other race. But unless we are content
with the prospect of one or the other of these issues, the only
possibility left is that of a positive Christian society. The third
will only commend itself to those who agree in their view of the
present situation, and who can see that a thoroughgoing secularism would be objectionable, in its consequences, even to those
who attach no positive importance to the survival of
Christianity for its own sake.

I am not investigating the possible lines of action by which
such a Christian society could be brought into being. I shall
confine myself to a slight outline of what I conceive to be
essential features of this society, bearing in mind that it can
neither be medieval in form, nor be modelled on the seventeenth
century or any previous age. In what sense, if any, can we speak

of a 'Christian State'? I would ask to be allowed to use the following working distinctions: the Christian State, the Christian Community, and the Community of Christians, as elements of the Christian Society.

I conceive then of the Christian State as of the Christian Society under the aspect of legislation, public administration, legal tradition, and form. Observe that at this point I am not approaching the problem of Church and State except with the question: with what kind of State can the Church have a relation? By this I mean a relation of the kind which has hitherto obtained in England; which is neither merely reciprocal tolerance, nor a Concordat. The latter seems to me merely a kind of compromise, of doubtful durability, resting on a dubious division of authority, and often a popular division of loyalty; a compromise which implies perhaps a hope on the part of the rulers of the State that their rule will outlast Christianity, and a faith on the part of the Church that it will survive any particular form of secular organization. A relation between Church and State such as is, I think, implied in our use of the term, implies that the State is in some sense Christian. It must be clear that I do not mean by a Christian State one in which the rulers are chosen because of their qualifications, still less their eminence, as Christians. A regiment of Saints is apt to be too uncomfortable to last. I do not deny that some advantages may accrue from persons in authority, in a Christian State, being Christians. Even in the present conditions, that sometimes happens; but even if, in the present conditions, *all* persons in positions of the highest authority were devout and orthodox Christians, we should not expect to see very much difference in the conduct of affairs. The Christian and the unbeliever do not, and cannot, behave very differently in the exercise of office; for it is the general ethos of the people they have to govern, not their own piety, that determines the behaviour of politicians. One may even accept F. S. Oliver's affirmation—following Buelow, following Disraeli—that real statesmen are inspired by nothing else than their instinct for power and their love of country. It is not primarily the Christianity of the statesmen that matters, but their being confined, by the temper and traditions of the people which they rule, to a Christian framework within which to realize their ambitions and advance the prosperity and prestige of their country. They may frequently perform un-Christian acts; they must never attempt to defend their actions on un-Christian principles.

The rulers and would-be rulers of modern states may be divided into three kinds, in a classification which cuts across the division of Fascism, Communism and democracy. There are such as have taken over or adapted some philosophy, as of Marx or Aquinas. There are those who, combining invention with eclecticism, have devised their own philosophy—not usually distinguished by either the profundity or the consistency one expects of a philosophy of life—and there are those who pursue their tasks without appearing to have any philosophy at all. I should not expect the rulers of a Christian State to be philosophers, or to be able to keep before their minds at every moment of decision the maxim that the life of virtue is the purpose of human society—*virtuosa ... vita est congregationis humanae finis*; but they would neither be self-educated, nor have been submitted in their youth merely to that system of miscellaneous or specialized instruction which passes for education: they would have received a Christian education. The purpose of a Christian education would not be merely to make men and women pious Christians: a system which aimed too rigidly at this end alone would become only obscurantist. A Christian education would primarily train people to be able to think in Christian categories, though it could not compel belief and would not impose the necessity for insincere profession of belief. What the rulers believed, would be less important than the beliefs to which they would be obliged to conform. And a sceptical or indifferent statesman, working within a Christian frame, might be more effective than a devout Christian statesman obliged to conform to a secular frame. For he would be required to design his policy for the government of a Christian Society.

The relation of the Christian State, the Christian Community, and the Community of Christians, may be looked at in connexion with the problem of *belief*. Among the men of state, you would have as a minimum, conscious conformity of behaviour. In the Christian Community that they ruled, the Christian faith would be ingrained, but it requires, as a minimum, only a largely unconscious behaviour; and it is only from the much smaller number of conscious human beings, the Community of Christians, that one would expect a conscious Christian life on its highest social level.

For the great mass of humanity whose attention is occupied mostly by their direct relation to the soil, or the sea, or the machine, and to a small number of persons, pleasures and duties, two conditions are required. The first is that, as their capacity for *thinking* about the objects of faith is small, their Christianity may be almost wholly realized in behaviour: both in their customary and periodic religious observances, and in a traditional code of behaviour towards their neighbours. The second is that, while they should have some perception of how far their lives fall short of Christian ideals, their religious and social life should form for them a natural whole, so that the difficulty of behaving as Christians should not impose an intolerable strain. These two conditions are really the same differently stated; they are far from being realized today.

The traditional unit of the Christian Community in England is the parish. I am not here concerned with the problem of how radically this system must be modified to suit a future state of things. The parish is certainly in decay, from several causes of which the least cogent is the division into sects: a much more important reason is urbanization—in which I am including also *sub*-urbanization, and all the causes and effects of urbanization. How far the parish must be superseded will depend largely upon our view of the necessity of accepting the causes which tend to destroy it. In any case, the parish will serve my purpose as an example of community unit. For this unit must not be solely religious, and not solely social; nor should the individual be a member of two separate, or even overlapping units, one religious and the other social. The unitary community should be religious-social, and it must be one in which all classes, if you have classes, have their centre of interest. That is a state of affairs which is no longer wholly realized except in very primitive tribes indeed.

It is a matter of concern not only in this country, but has been mentioned with concern by the late Supreme Pontiff, speaking not of one country but of all civilized countries, that the masses of the people have become increasingly alienated from Christianity. In an industrialized society like that of England, I am surprised that the people retains as much Christianity as it does. For the great majority of the people—and I am not here thinking of social classes, but of intellectual strata—religion must be primarily a matter of behaviour and habit, must be integrated with its social life, with its business and its pleasures; and the specifically religious emotions must be a kind of extension and sanctification of the domestic and social emotions. Even for the most highly developed and conscious individual, living in the world, a consciously Christian direction of thought and feeling can only occur at particular moments during the day and during the week, and these moments themselves recur in consequence of formed habits; to be conscious, without remission, of a Christian and a non-Christian alternative at moments of choice, imposes a very great strain. The mass of the population, in a Christian society, should not be exposed to a way of life in which there is too sharp and frequent a conflict between what is easy for them or what their circumstances dictate and what is Christian. The compulsion to live in such a way that Christian behaviour is only possible in a restricted number of situations, is a very powerful force against Christianity; for behaviour is as potent to affect belief, as belief to affect behaviour.

I am not presenting any idyllic picture of the rural parish, either present or past, in taking as a norm, the idea of a small and mostly self-contained group attached to the soil and having its interests centred in a particular place, with a kind of unity which may be designed, but which also has to grow through generations. It is the idea, or ideal, of a community small enough to consist of a nexus of direct personal relationships, in which all iniquities and turpitudes will take the simple and easily appreciable form of wrong relations between one person and another. But at present not even the smallest community, unless so primitive as to present objectionable features of another kind, is so simplified as this; and I am not advocating any complete reversion to any earlier state of things, real or idealized. The example appears to offer no solution to the problem of industrial, urban and suburban life which is that of the majority of the population. In its religious organization, we may say that Christendom has remained fixed at the state of development suitable to a simple agricultural and piscatorial society, and that modern material organization—or if 'organization' sounds too complimentary, we will say 'complication'—has produced a world for which Christian social forms are imperfectly adapted. Even if we agree on this point, there are two simplifications of the problem which are suspect. One is to insist that the only salvation for society is to return to a simpler mode of life, scrapping all the constructions of the modern world that we can bring ourselves to dispense with. This is an extreme statement of the neo-Ruskinian view, which was put forward with much vigour by the late A. J. Penty. When one considers the large amount of determination in social structure, this policy appears Utopian: if such a way of life ever comes to pass, it will be—as may well happen in the long run—from natural causes, and not from the moral will of men. The other alternative is to accept the modern world as it is and simply try to adapt Christian social ideals to it. The latter resolves itself into a mere doctrine of expediency; and is a surrender of the faith that Christianity itself can play any part in shaping social forms. And it does not require a Christian attitude to perceive that the modern system of society has a great deal in it that is inherently bad.

We now reach a point from which there is a course that I do not propose to take; and as it is an obvious course, and to some may appear to be the main thoroughfare, I ought to explain as briefly as I can why I do not propose to take it. We are accustomed to make the distinction (though in practice we are frequently confused) between the evil which is present in human nature at all times and in all circumstances, and the evil in particular institutions at particular times and places, and which, though attributable to some individuals rather than others, or traceable to the cumulative deflection of the wills of many individuals throughout several generations, cannot at any moment be fastened upon particular persons. If we make the mistake of assuming that this kind of evil results from causes wholly beyond the human will, then we are liable to believe that only other non-human causes can change it. But we are equally likely to take another line, and to place all our hopes in the replacement of our machinery. Nevertheless, the lines of thought, which I am doing no more than indicate, for the realization of a Christian society, must lead us inevitably to face such problems as the hypertrophy of the motive of Profit into a social ideal, the distinction between the *use* of natural resources and their exploitation, the use of labour and its exploitation, the advantages unfairly accruing to the trader in contrast to the primary producer, the misdirection of the financial machine, the iniquity of usury, and other features of a commercialized society which must be scrutinized on Christian principles. In ignoring these problems, I am not taking refuge in a mere admission of incompetence, though the suspicion that I am incompetent might operate against the acceptance of any observations that I made; nor am I simply resigning them to the supposed technical authorities, for that would be a surrender of the primacy of ethics. My point is that, while there is a considerable measure of agreement that certain things are wrong, the question of how they should be put right is so extremely controversial, that any proposal is immediately countered by a dozen others; and in this context, attention would be concentrated on the imperfections of my proposals, and away from my main concern, the end to be attained. I confine myself therefore to the assertion, which I think few will dispute, that a great deal of the machinery of modern life is merely a sanction for un-Christian aims, that it is not only hostile to the conscious pursuit of the Christian life in the world by the few, but to the maintenance of any Christian society *of* the world. We must abandon the notion that the Christian should be content with freedom of cultus, and with suffering no worldly disabilities on account of his faith. How-ever bigoted the announcement may sound, the Christian can be satisfied with nothing less than a Christian organization of society—which is not the same thing as a society consisting exclusively of devout Christians. It would be a society in which the natural end of man—virtue and well-being in com-munity—is acknowledged for all, and the supernatural end—beatitude—for those who have the eyes to see it.

I do not wish, however, to abandon my previous point, that a Christian community is one in which there is a unified religious-social code of behaviour. It should not be necessary for the ordinary individual to be wholly conscious of what elements are distinctly religious and Christian, and what are merely social and identified with his religion by no logical implication. I am not requiring that the community should contain more 'good Christians' than one would expect to find under favourable conditions. The religious life of the people would be largely a matter of behaviour and conformity; social customs would take on religious sanctions; there would no doubt be many irrelevant accretions and local emphases and observances—which, if they went too far in eccentricity or superstition, it would be the business of the Church to correct, but which otherwise could make for social tenacity and coherence. The traditional way of life of the community would not be imposed by law, would have no sense of outward constraint, and would not be the result merely of the sum of individual belief and understanding.

The rulers, I have said, will, *qua* rulers, accept Christianity not simply as their own faith to guide their actions, but as the system under which they are to govern. The people will accept it as a matter of behaviour and habit. In the abstraction which I have erected, it is obvious that the tendency of the State is towards expediency that may become cynical manipulation, the tend-ency of the people towards intellectual lethargy and superstition. We need therefore what I have called 'the Community of Christians', by which I mean, not local groups, and not the Church in any one of its senses, unless we call it 'the Church within the Church'. These will be the consciously and thoughtfully practising Christians, especially those of intellectual and spiritual superiority. It will be remarked at once that this category bears some resemblance to what Coleridge has called 'the clerisy'—a term recently revived, and given a somewhat different application, by Mr Middleton Murry. I think that my 'Community of Christians' is somewhat different from either use of the term 'clerisy'. The content which Coleridge gave to the term, certainly, has been somewhat voided by time. You will remember that Coleridge included in the extension of meaning three classes: the universities and great schools of learning, the parochial pastorate, and the local schoolmasters. Coleridge's conception of the clerical function, and of its relation to education was formed in a world that has since been strangely altered: his insistence that clergy should be 'in the rule married men and heads of families' and his dark references to a foreign ecclesiastical power, now sound merely quaint; and he quite failed to recognize the enormous value which monastic orders can and should have in the community. The term which I use is meant to be at once wider and more restricted. In the field of education it is obvious that the conformity to Christian belief and the possession of Christian knowledge, can no longer be taken for granted; nor can the supremacy of the theologian be either expected or imposed in the same way. In any future Christian society that I can conceive, the educational system will be formed according to Christian presuppositions of what education—as distinct from mere instruction—is for; but the personnel will inevitably be mixed: one may even hope that the mixture may be a benefit to its intellectual vitality. The mixture will include persons of exceptional ability who may be indifferent or disbelieving; there will be room for a proportion of other persons professing other faiths than Christianity. The limitations imposed upon such persons would be similar to those imposed by social necessity upon the politician who, without being able to believe the Christian faith, yet has abilities to offer in the public service, with which his country could ill dispense.

It would be still more rash of me to embark upon a criticism of the contemporary ideals of education, than it is for me to venture to criticize politics; but it is not impertinent to remark upon the close relationship of educational theory and political theory. One would indeed be surprised to find the educational system and the political system of any country in complete disaccord; and what I have said about the negative character of our political philosophy should suggest a parallel criticism of our education, not as it is found in practice here or there, but in the assumptions about the nature and purpose of education which tend to affect practice throughout the country. And I do not need to remind you that a pagan totalitarian government is hardly likely to leave education to look after itself, or to refrain from interfering with the traditional methods of the oldest institutions: of some of the results abroad of such interference on the most irrelevant grounds we are quite well aware. There is likely to be, everywhere, more and more pressure of circumstance towards adapting educational ideals to political ideals, and in the one as in the other sphere, we have only to choose between a higher and a lower rationalization. In a Christian society education must be religious, not in the sense that it will be administered by ecclesiastics, still less in the sense that it will exercise pressure, or attempt to instruct everyone in theology, but in the sense that its aims will be directed by a Christian philosophy of life. It will no longer be merely a term comprehending a variety of unrelated subjects undertaken for special purposes or for none at all.

My Community of Christians, then, in contrast to Coleridge's clerisy, could hardly include the whole of the teaching body. On the other hand, it would include, besides many of the laity engaged in various occupations, many, but not all, of the clergy. A national clergy must of course include individual priests of different intellectual types and levels; and, as I suggested before, belief has a vertical as well as a horizontal measurement: to answer fully the question 'What does A believe?' one must know enough about A to have some notion of the level on which he is capable of believing anything. The Community of Christians—a body of very nebulous outline—would contain both clergy and laity of superior intellectual and/or spiritual gifts. And it would include some of those who are ordinarily spoken of, not always with flattering intention, as 'intellectuals'.

That culture and the cultivation of philosophy and the arts should be confined to the cloister would be a decline into a Dark Age that I shudder to contemplate; on the other hand the segregation of lay 'intellectuals' into a world of their own, which very few ecclesiastics or politicians either penetrate or have any curiosity about, is not a progressive situation either. A good deal of waste seems to me to occur through pure ignorance; a great deal of ingenuity is expended on half-baked philosophies, in the absence of any common background of knowledge. We write for our friends—most of whom are also writers—or for our pupils—most of whom are going to be writers; or we aim at a hypothetical popular audience which we do not know and which perhaps does not exist. The result, in any case, is apt to be a refined provincial crudity. What are the most fruitful social conditions for the production of works of the first order, philosophical, literary or in the other arts, is perhaps one of those topics of controversy more suitable for conversation than for writing about. There may perhaps be no one set of conditions most suitable for the efflorescence of all these activities; it is equally possible that the necessary conditions may vary from one country and civilization to another. The regime of Louis XIV or of the Tudors and Stuarts could hardly be called libertarian; on the other hand, the rule of authoritarian governments in our time does not appear conducive to a renascence of the arts. Whether the arts flourish best in a period of growth and expansion, or in one of decay, is a question that I cannot answer. A strong and even tyrannous government may do no harm, so long as the sphere of its control is strictly limited; so long as it limits itself to restricting the liberties, without attempting to influence the minds, of its subjects; but a regime of unlimited demagogy appears to be stultifying. I must restrict my consideration to the position of the arts in our present society, and to what it should be in such a future society as I envisage.

It may be that the conditions unfavourable to the arts today lie too deep and are too extensive to depend upon the differences between one form of government and another; so that the prospect before us is either of slow continuous decay or of sudden extinction. You cannot, in any scheme for the reformation of society, aim directly at a condition in which the arts will flourish: these activities are probably by-products for which we cannot deliberately arrange the conditions. On the other hand, their decay may always be taken as a symptom of some social ailment to be investigated. The future of art and thought in a democratic society does not appear any brighter than any other, unless democracy is to mean something very different from anything actual. It is not that I would defend a moral censorship: I have always expressed strong objections to the suppression of books possessing, or even laying claim to literary merit. But what is more insidious than any censorship, is the steady influence which operates silently in any mass society organized for profit, for the depression of standards of art and culture. The increasing organization of advertisement and propaganda—or the influencing of masses of men by any means except through their intelligence—is all against them. The economic system is against them; the chaos of ideals and confusion of thought in our large scale mass education is against them; and against them also is the disappearance of any class of people who recognize public and private responsibility of patronage of the best that is made and written. At a period in which each nation has less and less 'culture' for its own consumption, all are making furious efforts to export their culture, to impress upon each other their achievements in arts which they are ceasing to cultivate or understand. And just as those who should be the intellectuals regard theology as a special study, like numismatics or heraldry, with which they need not concern themselves, and theologians observe the same indifference to literature and art, as special studies which do not concern *them*, so our political classes regard both fields as territories of which they have no reason to be ashamed of remaining in complete ignorance. Accordingly the more serious authors have a limited, and even provincial audience, and the more popular write for an illiterate and uncritical mob.

You cannot expect continuity and coherence in politics, you cannot expect reliable behaviour on fixed principles persisting through changed situations, unless there is an underlying political philosophy: not of a party, but of the nation. You cannot expect continuity and coherence in literature and the arts, unless you have a certain uniformity of culture, expressed in education by a settled, though not rigid agreement as to what everyone should know to some degree, and a positive distinction—however undemocratic it may sound—between the educated and the uneducated. I observed in America, that with a very high level of intelligence among undergraduates, progress was impeded by the fact that one could never assume that any two, unless they had been at the same school under the influence of the same masters at the same moment, had studied the same subjects or read the same books, though the number of subjects in which they had been instructed was surprising. Even with a smaller amount of total information, it might have been better if they had read fewer, but the same books. In a negative liberal society you have no agreement as to there being any body of knowledge which any educated person should have acquired at any particular stage: the idea of wisdom disappears, and you get sporadic and unrelated experimentation. A nation's system of education is much more important than its system of government; only a proper system of education can unify the active and the contemplative life, action and speculation, politics and the arts. But 'education', said Coleridge, 'is to be reformed, and defined as synonymous with instruction.' This revolution has been effected: to the populace education *means* instruction. The next step to be taken by the clericalism of secularism, is the inculcation of the political principles approved by the party in power.

I may seem to have wandered from my course, but it seemed necessary to mention the capital responsibility of education in the condition which we find or anticipate: a state secularized, a community turned into a mob, and a clerisy disintegrated. The obvious secularist solution for muddle is to subordinate everything to political power: and in so far as this involves the subordination of the money-making interests to those of the nation as a whole, it offers some immediate, though perhaps illusory relief: a people feels at least more dignified if its hero is the statesman however unscrupulous, or the warrior however brutal, rather than the financier. But it also means the confinement of the clergy to a more and more restricted field of activity, the subduing of free intellectual speculation, and the debauching of the arts by political criteria. It is only in a society with a religious basis—which is not the same thing as an ecclesiastical despotism—that you can get the proper harmony and tension, for the individual or for the community.

In any Christian society which can be imagined for the future—in what M. Maritain calls a *pluralist* society—my 'Community of Christians' cannot be a body of the definite vocational outline of the 'clerisy' of Coleridge: which, viewed in a hundred years' perspective, appears to approximate to the rigidity of a caste. The Community of Christians is not an organization, but a body of indefinite outline; composed of both clergy and laity, of the more conscious, more spiritually and intellectually developed of both. It will be their identity of belief and aspiration, their background of a common system of education and a common culture, which will enable them to influence and be influenced by each other, and collectively to form the conscious mind and the conscience of the nation.

The Spirit descends in different ways, and I cannot foresee any future society in which we could classify Christians and non-Christians simply by their professions of belief, or even, by any rigid code, by their behaviour. In the present ubiquity of ignorance, one cannot but suspect that many who call themselves Christians do not understand what the word means, and that some who would vigorously repudiate Christianity are more Christian than many who maintain it. And perhaps there will always be individuals who, with great creative gifts of value to mankind, and the sensibility which such gifts imply, will yet remain blind, indifferent, or even hostile. That must not disqualify them from exercising the talents they have been given.

The foregoing sketch of a Christian society, from which are

omitted many details that will be considered essential, could not stand even as a rough sketch—an *ébauche*—without some treatment, according to the same economy, of the relation of Church and State in such a society. So far, nothing has suggested the existence of an organized Church at all. But the State would remain under the necessity of respecting Christian principles, only so far as the habits and feelings of the people were not too suddenly affronted or too violently outraged, or so far as it was deterred by any univocal protest of the most influential of the Community of Christians. The State is Christian only negatively; its Christianity is a reflection of the Christianity of the society which it governs. We have no safeguard against its proceeding, from un-Christian acts, to action on implicitly un-Christian principles, and thence to action on avowedly un-Christian principles. We have no safeguard for the purity of our Christianity; for, as the State may pass from expediency to lack of principle, and as the Christian Community may sink into torpor, so the Community of Christians may be debilitated by group or individual eccentricity and error. So far, we have only a society such that it can have a significant relation to a Church; a relationship which is not of hostility or even of accommodation. And this relation is so important that without discussing it we have not even shown the assembled skeleton of a Christian Society, we have only exposed the unarticulated bones.

III

I have spoken of this essay as being, in one aspect, a kind of preface to the problem of Church and State; it is as well, at this point, to indicate its prefatorial limitations. The problem is one of concern to every Christian country—that is, to every possible form of Christian society. It will take a different form according to the traditions of that society—Roman, Orthodox, or Lutheran. It will take still another form in those countries, obviously the United States of America and the Dominions, where the variety of races and religious communions represented appears to render the problem insoluble. Indeed, for these latter countries the problem might not appear even to exist; these countries might appear to be committed from their origin to a neutral form of society. I am not ignoring the possibility of a neutral society, under such conditions, persisting indefinitely. But I believe that if these countries are to develop a positive culture of their own, and not remain merely derivatives of Europe, they can only proceed either in the direction of a pagan or of a Christian society. I am not suggesting that the latter alternative must lead to the forcible suppression, or to the complete disappearance of dissident sects; still less, I hope, to a superficial union of Churches under an official exterior, a union in which theological differences would be so belittled that its Christianity might become wholly bogus. But a positive culture must have a positive set of values, and the dissentients must remain marginal, tending to make only marginal contributions.

However dissimilar the local conditions, therefore, this question of Church and State is of importance everywhere. Its actuality in Europe may make it appear all the more remote in America, just as its actuality in England raises a number of considerations remote to the rest of Europe. But if what I say in the following pages has its direct application only in England, it is not because I am thinking of local matters without relation to Christendom as a whole. It is partly that I can only discuss profitably the situations with which I am most familiar, and partly that a more generalized consideration would appear to deal only with figments and fancies. I have therefore limited my field to the possibility of a Christian society in England, and in speaking of Church and State it is the Anglican Church that I have in mind. But it must be remembered that such terms as 'Establishment' and 'Established Church' can have a wider meaning than we ordinarily give them. On the other hand, I only mean such a Church as can claim to represent the traditional form of Christian belief and worship of the great mass of the people of a particular country.

If my outline of a Christian society has commanded the assent of the reader, he will agree that such a society can only be realized when the great majority of the sheep belong to one fold. To those who maintain that unity is a matter of indifference, to those who maintain even that a diversity of theological views is a good thing to an indefinite degree, I can make no appeal. But if the desirability of unity be admitted, if the idea of a Christian society be grasped and accepted, then it can only be realized, in England, through the Church of England. This is not the place for discussing the theological position of that Church: if in any points it is wrong, inconsistent, or evasive, these are matters for reform within the Church. And I am not overlooking the possibility and hope of eventual reunion or re-integration, on one side and another; I am only affirming that it is this Church which, by reason of its tradition, its organization, and its relation in the past to the religious-social life of the people, is the one for our purpose—and that no Christianization of England can take place without it.

The Church of a Christian society, then, should have some relation to the three elements in a Christian society that I have named. It must have a hierarchical organization in direct and official relation to the State: in which relation it is always in danger of sinking into a mere department of State. It must have an organization, such as the parochial system, in direct contact with the smallest units of the community and their individual members. And finally, it must have, in the persons of its more intellectual, scholarly and devout officers, its masters of ascetic theology and its men of wider interests, a relation to the Community of Christians. In matters of dogma, matters of faith and morals, it will speak as the final authority within the nation; in more mixed questions it will speak through individuals. At times, it can and should be in conflict with the State, in rebuking derelictions in policy, or in defending itself against encroachments of the temporal power, or in shielding the community against tyranny and asserting its neglected rights, or in contesting heretical opinion or immoral legislation and administration. At times, the hierarchy of the Church may be under attack from the Community of Christians, or from groups within it: for any organization is always in danger of corruption and in need of reform from within.

Although I am not here concerned with the means by which a Christian society could be brought about, it is necessary always to consider the idea in relation to particular existing societies; because one does not expect or desire that its constitution would be identical in all Christian countries. I do not assume that the relation of Church and State in England, either as it is or as it might be, is a model for all other communities. Whether an 'Establishment' is the best relation in the abstract, is nowhere my question. Were there no Establishment in England, we should have to examine its desirability. But as we have the Establishment, we must take the situation as we find it, and consider for a moment the merits of the problem of Disestablishment. The advocates of this course, within the Church, have many cogent reasons to expose: the abuses and scandals which such a change might remedy, the inconsistencies which might be removed, and the advantages which might accrue, are too patent to require mention. That abuses and defects of another kind might make their appearance in a disestablished Church, is a possibility which has not perhaps received enough attention. But what is much more to my point is the gravity of the abdication which the Church—whether voluntarily or under pressure—would be making. Setting aside the anomalies which might be corrected without going to that length, I will admit that an Established Church is exposed to peculiar temptations and compulsions: it has greater advantages and greater difficulties. But we must pause to reflect that a Church, once disestablished, cannot easily be re-established, and that the very act of disestablishment separates it more definitely and irrevocably from the life of the nation than if it had never been established. The effect on the mind of the people of the visible and dramatic withdrawal of the Church from the affairs of the nation, of the deliberate recognition of two standards and ways of life, of the Church's abandonment of all those who are not by their wholehearted profession within the fold—this is incalculable; the risks are so great that such an act can be nothing but a desperate measure. It appears to assume something which I am not yet ready to take for granted: that the division between Christians and non-Christians in this country is already, or is determined to become, so clear that it can be reduced to statistics. But if one believes, as I do, that the great majority of people are neither one thing nor the other, but are living in a no man's land, then the situation looks very different; and disestablishment instead of being the *recognition* of a condition at which we have arrived, would be the *creation* of a condition the results of which we cannot foresee.

With the reform of the Establishment I am not here concerned: the discussion of that requires a familiarity with constitutional, canon, and civil law. But I do not think that the argument from the prosperity of the Disestablished Church of Wales, sometimes brought forward by advocates of disestablishment, is to the point. Apart from the differences of racial temperament which must be taken into account, the full effect of disestablishment cannot be seen from the illustration of a small part of the island; and, if disestablishment were made general, the full effect would not appear at once. And I think that the tendency of the time is opposed to the view that the religious and the secular life of the individual and the community can form two separate and autonomous domains. I know that a theology of the absolute separation of the life of the Spirit and the life of the World has spread from Germany. Such a doctrine appears more plausible, when the Church's position is wholly defensive, when it is subject to daily persecution, when its spiritual claims are questioned and when its immediate necessity is to keep itself alive and to keep its doctrine pure. But this theology is incompatible with the assumptions underlying everything that I have been saying. The increasing complexity of modern life renders it unacceptable, for, as I have already said, we are faced with vital problems arising not merely out of the necessity of cooperating with non-Christians, but out of our unescapable implication in non-Christian institutions and systems. And finally, the totalitarian tendency is against it, for the tendency of totalitarianism is to re-affirm, on a lower level, the religious-social nature of society.

And I am convinced that you cannot have a national Christian society, a religious-social community, a society with a political philosophy founded upon the Christian faith, if it is constituted as a mere congeries of private and independent sects. The national faith must have an official recognition by the State, as well as an accepted status in the community and a basis of conviction in the heart of the individual.

Heresy is often defined as an insistence upon one half of the truth; it can also be an attempt to simplify the truth, by reducing it to the limits of our ordinary understanding, instead of enlarging our reason to the apprehension of truth. Monotheism or tritheism is easier to grasp than trinitarianism. We have observed the lamentable results of the attempt to isolate the Church from the World; there are also instances of the failure of the attempt to integrate the World in the Church; we must also be on guard against the attempt to integrate the Church in the World. A permanent danger of an established Church is Erastianism: we do not need to refer to the eighteenth century, or to pre-war Russia, to remind ourselves of that. Deplorable as such a situation is, it is not so much the immediate and manifest scandals but the ultimate consequences of Erastianism that are the most serious offences. By alienating the mass of the people from orthodox Christianity, by leading them to identify the Church with the actual hierarchy and to suspect it of being an instrument of oligarchy or class, it leaves men's minds exposed to varieties of irresponsible and irreflective enthusiasm followed by a second crop of paganism.

The danger of a National Church becoming a class Church, is not one that concerns us immediately today; for now that it is possible to be respectable without being a member of the Church of England, or a Christian of any kind, it is also possible to be a member of the Church of England without being—in that sense—respectable. The danger that a National Church might become also a nationalistic Church is one to which our predecessors theorizing about Church and State could hardly have been expected to devote attention, since the danger of nationalism itself, and the danger of the supersession of every form of Christianity, could not have been very present to their minds. Yet the danger was always there: and, for some persons still, Rome is associated with the Armada and Kingsley's *Westward Ho!*. For a National Church tends to reflect only the religious-social habits of the nation; and its members, in so far as they are isolated from the Christian communities of other nations, may tend to lose all criteria by which to distinguish, in their own religious-social complex, between what is universal and what is local, accidental, and erratic. Within limits, the cultus of the universal Church may quite properly vary according to the racial temperaments and cultural traditions of each nation. Roman Catholicism is not quite the same thing (to the eye of the sociologist, if not to that of the theologian) in Spain, France, Ireland and the United States of America, and but for central authority it would differ much more widely. The tendency to differ may be as strong among bodies of the same communion in different countries, as among various sects within the same country; and, indeed, the sects within one country may be expected to show traits in common, which none of them will share with the same communion abroad.

The evils of nationalistic Christianity have, in the past, been mitigated by the relative weakness of national consciousness and the strength of Christian tradition. They have not been wholly absent: missionaries have sometimes been accused of propagating (through ignorance, not through cunning) the customs and attitudes of the social groups to which they have belonged, rather than giving the natives the essentials of the Christian faith in such a way that they might harmonize their own culture with it. On the other hand, I think that some events during the last twenty-five years have led to an increasing recognition of the supra-national Christian society: for if that is not marked by such conferences as those of Lausanne, Stockholm, Oxford, Edinburgh—and also Malines—then I do not know of what use these conferences have been. The purpose of the labours involved in arranging intercommunion between the official Churches of certain countries is not merely to provide reciprocal sacramental advantages for travellers, but to affirm the Universal

Church on earth. Certainly, no one today can defend the idea of a National Church, without balancing it with the idea of the Universal Church, and without keeping in mind that truth is one and that theology has no frontiers.

I think that the dangers to which a National Church is exposed, when the Universal Church is no more than a pious ideal, are so obvious that only to mention them is to command assent. Completely identified with a particular people, the National Church may at all times, but especially at moments of excitement, become no more than the voice of that people's prejudice, passion or interest. But there is another danger, not quite so easily identified. I have maintained that the idea of a Christian society implies, for me, the existence of one Church which shall *aim at* comprehending the whole nation. Unless it has this aim, we relapse into that conflict between citizenship and church-membership, between public and private morality, which today makes moral life so difficult for everyone, and which in turn provokes that craving for a simplified, monistic solution of statism or racism which the National Church can only combat if it recognizes its position as a part of the Universal Church. But if we allowed ourselves to entertain for Europe (to confine our attention to that continent) the ideal merely of a kind of society of Christian societies, we might tend unconsciously to treat the idea of the Universal Church as only the idea of a supernatural League of Nations. The direct allegiance of the individual would be to his National Church alone, and the Universal Church would remain an abstraction or become a cockpit for conflicting national interests. But the difference between the Universal Church and a perfected League of Nations is this, that the allegiance of the individual to his own Church is secondary to his allegiance to the Universal Church. Unless the National Church is a part of the whole, it has no claim upon me: but a League of Nations which could have a claim upon the devotion of the individual, prior to the claim of his country, is a chimaera which very few persons can even have endeavoured to picture to themselves. I have spoken more than once of the intolerable position of those who try to lead a

Christian life in a non-Christian world. But it must be kept in mind that even in a Christian society as well organized as we can conceive possible in this world, the limit would be that our temporal and spiritual life should be harmonized: the temporal and spiritual would never be identified. There would always remain a dual allegiance, to the State and to the Church, to one's countrymen and to one's fellow-Christians everywhere, and the latter would always have the primacy. There would always be a tension; and this tension is essential to the idea of a Christian society, and is a distinguishing mark between a Christian and a pagan society.

IV

It should be obvious that the form of political organization of a Christian State does not come within the scope of this discussion. To identify any particular form of government with Christianity is a dangerous error: for it confounds the permanent with the transitory, the absolute with the contingent. Forms of government, and of social organization, are in constant process of change, and their operation may be very different from the theory which they are supposed to exemplify. A theory of the State may be, explicitly or implicitly, anti-Christian: it may arrogate rights which only the Church is entitled to claim, or pretend to decide moral questions on which only the Church is qualified to pronounce. On the other hand, a regime may in practice claim either more or less than it professes, and we have to examine its working as well as its constitution. We have no assurance that a democratic regime might not be as inimical to Christianity in practice, as another might be in theory: and the best government must be relative to the character and the stage of intelligence and education of a particular people in a particular place at a particular time. Those who consider that a discussion of the nature of a Christian society should conclude by supporting a particular form of political organization, should ask themselves whether they really believe our form of government to be more important than our Christianity; and those who are convinced that the present form of government of Britain is the one most suitable for any Christian people, should ask themselves whether they are confusing a Christian society with a society in which individual Christianity is tolerated.

This essay is not intended to be either an anti-Communist or an anti-Fascist manifesto; the reader may by this time have forgotten what I said at the beginning, to the effect that I was less concerned with the more superficial, though important differences between the regiment of different nations, than with the more profound differences between pagan and Christian society. Our preoccupation with foreign politics during the last few years has induced a surface complacency rather than a consistent attempt at self-examination of conscience. Sometimes we are almost persuaded that we are getting on very nicely, with a reform here and a reform there, and would have been getting on still better, if only foreign governments did not insist upon breaking all the rules and playing what is really a different game. What is more depressing still is the thought that only fear or jealousy of foreign success can alarm us about the health of our own nation; that only through this anxiety can we see such things as depopulation, malnutrition, moral deterioration, the decay of agriculture, as evils at all. And what is worst of all is to advocate Christianity, not because it is true, but because it might be beneficial. Towards the end of 1938 we experienced a wave of revivalism which should teach us that folly is not the prerogative of any one political party or any one religious communion, and that hysteria is not the privilege of the uneducated. The Christianity expressed has been vague, the religious fervour has been a fervour for democracy. It may engender nothing better than a disguised and peculiarly sanctimonious nationalism, accelerating our progress towards the paganism which we say we abhor. To justify Christianity because it provides a foundation of morality, instead of showing the necessity of Christian morality from the truth of Christianity, is a very dangerous inversion; and we may reflect, that a good deal of the attention of totalitarian states has been devoted, with a steadiness of purpose not always found in democracies, to providing their national life with a foundation of morality—the wrong kind perhaps, but a good deal more of it. It is not enthusiasm, but dogma, that differentiates a Christian from a pagan society.

I have tried to restrict my ambition of a Christian society to a social minimum: to picture, not a society of saints, but of ordinary men, of men whose Christianity is communal before being individual. It is very easy for speculation on a possible Christian order in the future to tend to come to rest in a kind of apocalyptic vision of a golden age of virtue. But we have to remember that the Kingdom of Christ on earth will never be realized, and also that it is always being realized; we must remember that whatever reform or revolution we carry out, the result will always be a sordid travesty of what human society should be—though the world is never left wholly without glory. In such a society as I imagine, as in any that is not petrified, there will be innumerable seeds of decay. Any human scheme for society is realized only when the great mass of humanity has become adapted to it; but this adaptation becomes also, insensibly, an adaptation of the scheme itself to the mass on which it operates: the overwhelming pressure of mediocrity, sluggish and indomitable as a glacier, will mitigate the most violent, and depress the most exalted revolution, and what is realized is so unlike the end that enthusiasm conceived, that foresight would weaken the effort. A wholly Christian society might be a society for the most part on a low level; it would engage the cooperation of many whose Christianity was spectral or superstitious or feigned, and of many whose motives were primarily worldly and selfish. It would require constant reform.

I should not like it to be thought, however, that I considered the presence of the higher forms of devotional life to be a matter of minor importance for such a society. I have, it is true, insisted upon the communal, rather than the individual aspect: a community of men and women, not individually better than they are now, except for the capital difference of holding the Christian faith. But their holding the Christian faith would give them something else which they lack: a *respect* for the religious life, for

79

the life of prayer and contemplation, and for those who attempt to practise it. In this I am asking no more of the British Christian, than is characteristic of the ordinary Moslem or Hindu. But the ordinary man would need the opportunity to know that the religious life existed, that it was given its due place, would need to recognize the profession of those who have abandoned the world, as he recognizes the professions practised in it. I cannot conceive a Christian society without religious orders, even purely contemplative orders, even enclosed orders. And, incidentally, I should not like the 'Community of Christians' of which I have spoken, to be thought of as merely the nicest, most intelligent and public-spirited of the upper middle class—it is not to be conceived on that analogy.

We may say that religion, as distinguished from modern paganism, implies a life in conformity with nature. It may be observed that the natural life and the supernatural life have a conformity to each other which neither has with the mechanistic life: but so far has our notion of what is natural become distorted, that people who consider it 'unnatural' and therefore repugnant, that a person of either sex should elect a life of celibacy, consider it perfectly 'natural' that families should be limited to one or two children. It would perhaps be more natural, as well as in better conformity with the Will of God, if there were more celibates and if those who were married had larger families. But I am thinking of 'conformity to nature' in a wider sense than this. We are being made aware that the organization of society on the principle of private profit, as well as public destruction, is leading both to the deformation of humanity by unregulated industrialism, and to the exhaustion of natural resources, and that a good deal of our material progress is a progress for which succeeding generations may have to pay dearly. I need only mention, as an instance now very much before the public eye, the results of 'soil-erosion'—the exploitation of the earth, on a vast scale for two generations, for commercial profit: immediate benefits leading to dearth and desert. I would not have it thought that I condemn a society because of its material ruin, for that would be to make its material success a sufficient test of its excellence; I mean only that a wrong attitude towards nature implies, somewhere, a wrong attitude towards God, and that the consequence is an inevitable doom. For a long enough time we have believed in nothing but the values arising in a mechanized, commercialized, urbanized way of life: it would be as well for us to face the permanent conditions upon which God allows us to live upon this planet. And without sentimentalizing the life of the savage, we might practise the humility to observe, in some of the societies upon which we look down as primitive or back-ward, the operation of a social-religious-artistic complex which we should emulate upon a higher plane. We have been accus-tomed to regard 'progress' as always integral; and have yet to learn that it is only by an effort and a discipline, greater than society has yet seen the need of imposing upon itself, that material knowledge and power is gained without loss of spiritual knowledge and power. The struggle to recover the sense of relation to nature and to God, the recognition that even the most primitive feelings should be part of our heritage, seems to me to be the explanation and justification of the life of D. H. Lawrence, and the excuse for his aberrations. But we need not only to learn how to look at the world with the eyes of a Mexican Indian—and I hardly think that Lawrence succeeded—and we certainly cannot afford to stop there. We need to know how to see the world as the Christian Fathers saw it; and the purpose of reascending to origins is that we should be able to return, with greater spiritual knowledge, to our own situation. We need to recover the sense of religious fear, so that it may be overcome by religious hope.

I should not like to leave the reader supposing that I have attempted to contribute one more amateur sketch of an abstract and impracticable future: the blue-print from which the doc-trinaire criticizes the piecemeal day-to-day efforts of political men. These latter efforts have to go on; but unless we can find a pattern in which all problems of life can have their place, we are only likely to go on complicating chaos. So long, for instance, as we consider finance, industry, trade, agriculture merely as com-peting interests to be reconciled from time to time as best they may, so long as we consider 'education' as a good in itself of which everyone has a right to the utmost, without any ideal of the good life for society or for the individual, we shall move from one uneasy compromise to another. To the quick and simple organization of society for ends which, being only material and worldly, must be as ephemeral as worldly success, there is only one alternative. As political philosophy derives its sanction from ethics, and ethics from the truth of religion, it is only by returning to the eternal source of truth that we can hope for any social organization which will not, to its ultimate destruction, ignore some essential aspect of reality. The term 'democracy', as I have said again and again, does not contain enough positive content to stand alone against the forces that you dislike—it can easily be transformed by them. If you will not have God (and He is a jealous God) you should pay your respects to Hitler or Stalin.

I believe that there must be many persons who, like myself, were deeply shaken by the events of September 1938, in a way from which one does not recover; persons to whom that month brought a profounder realization of a general plight. It was not a disturbance of the understanding: the events themselves were not surprising. Nor, as became increasingly evident, was our distress due merely to disagreement with the policy and behaviour of the moment. The feeling which was new and unexpected was a feeling of humiliation, which seemed to demand an act of personal contrition, of humility, repentance and amendment; what had happened was something in which one was deeply implicated and responsible. It was not, I repeat, a criticism of the government, but a doubt of the validity of a civilization. We could not match conviction with conviction, we had no ideas with which we could either meet or oppose the ideas opposed to us. Was our society, which had always been so assured of its superiority and rectitude, so confident of its unexamined premises, assembled round anything more permanent than a congeries of banks, insurance companies and industries, and had it any beliefs more essential than a belief in compound interest and the maintenance of dividends? Such thoughts as these formed the starting point, and must remain the excuse, for saying what I have had to say.

6 *September* 1939. The whole of this book, with Preface and Notes, was completed before it was known that we should be at war. But the possibility of war, which has now been realized, was always present to my mind, and the only additional observations which I feel called upon to make are these: first, that the alignment of forces which has now revealed itself should bring more clearly to our consciousness the alternative of Christianity or paganism; and, second, that we cannot afford to defer our constructive thinking to the conclusion of hostilities—a moment when, as we should know from experience, good counsel is liable to be obscured.

NOTES

Page 43. In using the term 'Idea' I have of course had in mind the definition given by Coleridge, when he lays down at the beginning of his *Church and State* that: 'By an idea I mean (in this instance) that conception of a thing, which is not abstracted from any particular state, form or mode, in which the thing may happen to exist at this or that time; nor yet generalized from any number or succession of such forms or modes; but which is given by the knowledge of its ultimate aim.'

P. 44. Christian sociologists. I am deeply indebted to several Christian economists and sociologists, both in England and elsewhere, and notably to R. H. Tawney. My difference of approach in these pages need not be further elaborated, but it is interesting to compare the treatment of the problem of Church and State by V. A. Demant in his very valuable *Christian Polity*, pp. 120 ff. and pp. 135 ff. Fr. Demant observes that the authority of the Church 'cannot now be claimed on the ground that it represents all citizens'. But while the Church does not represent all citizens in the sense in which a Member of Parliament may be said to 'represent' his constituents, even those who vote consistently against him, yet its function seems to me wider than only to 'safeguard the individual in his right to pursue certain purposes which are not political purposes'; what I am primarily concerned with throughout is not the responsibility of the Church towards the individual but towards the community. The relation of the Church with the State may be one of checks and balances, but the background and justification of this relation is the Church's relation to *Society*. Fr. Demant gives a very good account of the forces tending towards acceptance of the absolutist State, and remarks truly that: 'This fact of the secularization of human life does not arise mainly from the extension of the State's powers. This is rather the effort of the State to recover significance in the life of a people which has become disintegrated through the confusion of social means and ends which is its secularization.'

One of the causes of the totalitarian State is an effort of the State to supply a function which the Church has ceased to serve; to enter into a relation to the community which the Church has failed to maintain; which leads to the recognition as full citizens only of those who are prepared to accept it in this relation.

I agree cordially with Fr. Demant's observation that: 'The fact which renders most of our theories of Church and State irrelevant is the domination of politics by economics and finance; and this is most true in democratic states. The subservience of politics to plutocracy is the main fact about the State confronting the Church today.'

Fr. Demant is concerned with the reform of this situation, in a secular society; and with the right position of the Church in a secular society. But unless I have misunderstood him, he appears to me to take this secularization for granted. Assuming that our present society is neutral rather than non-Christian I am concerned with enquiring what it might be like if it took the Christian direction.

P. 51. 'Totalitarianism can retain the terms "freedom" and "democracy" and give them its own meaning.' A letter appeared in *The Times* (24 April 1939) from General J. F. C. Fuller, who, as *The Times* had previously stated, was one of the two British visitors invited to Herr Hitler's birthday celebrations. General Fuller states that he is 'a firm believer in the democracy of Mazzini, because he places duty to the nation before individual rights'. General Fuller calls himself a 'British Fascist', and believes that Britain 'must swim with the out-flowing tide of this great political change' (i.e. to a Fascist system of government).

From my point of view, General Fuller has as good a title to call himself a 'believer in democracy' as anyone else.

P. 52. Imitation *à rebours*. A column in the *Evening Standard* of 10 May 1939, headed *'Back to the Kitchen' Creed Denounced*, reported the annual conference of the Civil Service Clerical Association.

'Miss Bower of the Ministry of Transport, who moved that the association should take steps to obtain the removal of the ban (i.e. against married women Civil Servants) said it was wise to abolish an institution which embodied one of the main tenets of the Nazi creed—the relegation of women to the sphere of the kitchen, the children and the church.'

The report, by its abbreviation, may do less than justice to Miss Bower, but I do not think that I am unfair to the report, in finding the implication that what is Nazi is wrong, and need not be discussed on its own merits. Incidentally, the term 'relegation of women' prejudices the issue. Might one suggest that the kitchen, the children and the church could be considered to have a claim upon the attention of married women? Or that no normal married woman would prefer to be a wage-earner if she could help it? What is miserable is a system that makes the dual wage necessary.

P. 52. Fascist doctrine. I mean only such doctrine as asserts the absolute authority of the state, or the infallibility of a ruler. 'The corporative state', recommended by *Quadragesimo Anno*, is not in question. The economic organization of totalitarian states is not in question. The ordinary person does not object to Fascism because it is pagan, but because he is fearful of authority, even when it is pagan.

P. 52. The red herring of the German national religion. I cannot hold such a low opinion of German intelligence as to accept any stories of the revival of pre-Christian cults. I can, however, believe that the kind of religion expounded by Professor Wilhelm Hauer is really in existence—and I am very sorry to believe it. I rely upon the essay contributed by Dr Hauer to a very interesting volume, *Germany's New Religion* (Allen and Unwin, 1937), in which orthodox Lutheranism is defended by Karl Heim, and Catholicism by Karl Adam.

The religion of Hauer is deistic, claiming to 'worship a more than human God'. He believes it to be 'an eruption from the biological and spiritual depths of the German nation', and unless one is prepared to deny that the German nation has such depths, I do not see that the statement can be ridiculed. He believes that 'each new age must mould its own religious forms—alas, many persons in Anglo-Saxon countries hold the same belief. He professes himself to be particularly a disciple of Eckhart; and whether or not one believes that the doctrines condemned by the Church were what Eckhart strove to propagate, it is certainly the condemned doctrine that Hauer holds. He considers that the 'revolt of the German from Christianity reached its culmination in Nietzsche': many people would not limit that revolt to the German. He advocates tolerance. He objects to Christianity because 'it claims to possess the absolute truth, and with this claim is bound up the idea that men can only achieve salvation in one way, through Christ, and that it must send to the stake those whose faith and life do not conform, or pray for them till they quit the error of their ways for the kingdom of God.' Thousands of people in Western countries would agree with this attitude. He objects to sacramental religion, because 'everyone has an immediate relation to God, is, in fact, in the depths of his heart one with the eternal Ground of the world.' Faith comes not from revelation but from 'personal experience'. He is not interested in 'the mass of intellectuals', but in the 'multitudes of ordinary people' who are looking for 'Life'. 'We believe', he says, 'that God has laid a great task on our nation, and that he has therefore revealed himself specially in its history and will continue to do so.' To my ear, such phrases have a not altogether unfamiliar ring. Hauer believes also in something very popular in this country, the religion of the blue sky, the grass and flowers. He believes that Jesus (even if he was wholly Semitic on both sides) is one of the 'great figures who soar above the centuries'.

I have quoted so much, in order to let Professor Hauer declare himself for what he is: the end product of German Liberal Protestantism, a nationalistic Unitarian. Translated into English terms, he might be made to appear as simply a patriotic Modernist. The German National Religion, as Hauer expounds it, turns out to be something with which we are already familiar. So, if the German Religion is also your religion, the sooner you realize the fact the better.

P. 55. 'Hygienic morality'. M. Denis de Rougemont, in his remarkable book *L'Amour et l'occident*, has the sentence (p. 269) which is to the point: 'L'anarchie des moeurs et l'hygiène autoritaire agissent à peu près dans le même sens: elles déçoivent le besoin de passion, héréditaire ou acquis par la culture; elles détendent ses ressorts intimes et personnels.'

P. 55. It may be opportune at this point to say a word about the attitude of a Christian Society towards Pacifism. I am not concerned with rationalistic pacifism, or with humanitarian pacifism, but with Christian pacifism—that which asserts that all warfare is categorically forbidden to followers of Our Lord. This absolute Christian pacifism should be distinguished again from another: that which would assert that only a *Christian* society is worth fighting for, and that a particular society may fall so far short, or may be so positively anti-Christian, that no Christian will be justified or excused for fighting for it. With this relative Christian pacifism I cannot be concerned, because my hypothesis is that of a Christian society. In such a society, what will be the place of the Christian pacifist?

Such a person would continue to exist, as sects and individual vagaries would probably continue to exist; and it would be the duty of the Christian who was not a pacifist to treat the pacifist with consideration and respect. It would also be the duty of the State to treat him with consideration and respect, having assured itself of his sincerity. The man who believes that a particular war in which his country proposes to engage is an aggressive war, who believes that his country could refuse to take part in it without its legitimate interests being imperilled, and without failing in its duty to God and its neighbours, would be wrong to remain silent (the attitude of the late Charles Eliot Norton in regard to the Spanish–American War of 1898 is to the point). But I cannot but believe that the man who maintains that war is in all circumstances wrong, is in some way repudiating an obligation towards society; and in so far as the society is a Christian society the obligation is so much the more serious. Even if each particular war proves in turn to have been unjustified, yet the idea of a Christian society seems incompatible with the idea of absolute pacifism; for pacifism can only continue to flourish so long as the majority of persons forming a society are not pacifists; just as sectarianism can only flourish against the background of orthodoxy. The notion of communal responsibility, of the responsibility of every individual for the sins of the society to which he belongs, is one that needs to be more firmly apprehended; and if I share the guilt of my society in time of 'peace', I do not see how I can absolve myself from it in time of war, by abstaining from the common action.

P. 56. The Community of Christians. This term is perhaps open to objection. I did not wish to employ Coleridge's term 'clerisy' while altering its meaning, but I assume that the reader is familiar with 'clerisy' in his *Church and State*, and with Mr Middleton Murry's use of the same word. Perhaps the term 'Community of Christians' may connote to some a kind of esoteric *chapelle* or fraternity of the self-appointed, but I hope that what is said later in this chapter may prevent that inference. I wished to avoid excessive emphasis on nominal function, as it seemed to me that Coleridge's 'clerisy' might tend to become merely a brahminical *caste*.

I should add, as a note on the use of the phrase 'superior intellectual and/or spiritual gifts' (p. 64), that the possession of intellectual or spiritual gifts does not necessarily confer that intellectual understanding of spiritual issues which is the qualification for exerting the kind of influence here required. Nor is the person who possesses this qualification necessarily a 'better Christian' in his private life than the man whose insight is less profound; nor is he necessarily exempt from doctrinal error. I prefer that the definition should be, provisionally, too comprehensive rather than too narrow.

P. 63. Christian Education. This note, as well as that on 'The Community of Christians', is elicited by a searching comment by Bro. George Every, SSM, who has been so kind as to read this book in proof. Those who have read a paper called 'Modern Education and the Classics', written in a different context, and published in a volume entitled *Essays Ancient and Modern*, may assume that what I have in mind is simply the 'classical education' of earlier times. The problem of Education is too large to be considered in a brief book like this, and the question of the best curriculum is not here raised. I limit myself to the assertion that the miscellaneous curriculum will not do, and that education must be something more than the acquisition of information, technical competence, or superficial culture. Furthermore, I am not here concerned with what must occupy the mind of anyone approaching the subject of Education directly, that is the question of what should be done *now*. The point upon which all who are dissatisfied with contemporary Education can agree, is the necessity for criteria and values. But one must start by expelling from one's mind any mere prejudice or sentiment in favour of any previous system of education, and recognizing the differences between the society for which we have to legislate, and any form of society which we have known in the past.

P. 67. Uniformity of culture. In an important passage in *Beyond Politics* (pp. 23–31) Mr Christopher Dawson discusses the possibility of an 'organization of culture'. He recognizes that it is impossible to do this 'by any kind of philosophic or scientific dictatorship', or by a return 'to the old humanist discipline of letters, for that is inseparable from the aristocratic ideal of a privileged caste of scholars'. He asserts that 'a democratic society must find a correspondingly democratic organization of culture'; and finds that 'the form of organization appropriate to our society in the field of culture as well as in that of politics is the party—that is to say, a voluntary organization for common ends based on a common "ideology".'

I think that I am in close sympathy with Mr Dawson's aims, and yet I find it difficult to apprehend the meaning of this 'culture' which will have no philosophy (for philosophy, he reminds us, has lost its ancient prestige) and which will not be specifically religious. What, in the kind of society to which we are approximating, will be a 'democratic organization of culture'? To substitute for 'democratic' a term which for me has greater concreteness, I should say that the society which is coming into existence, and which is advancing in every country whether 'democratic' or 'totalitarian', is a lower-middle-class society: I should expect the culture of the twentieth century to belong to the lower middle class as that of the Victorian age belonged to the upper middle class or commercial aristocracy. If then for Mr Dawson's phrase we substitute the words 'a lower-middle-class society must find a correspondingly lower-middle-class organization of culture' we have something which seems to me to possess more meaning, though it leaves us in greater perplexity. And if Mr Dawson's Culture Party—about which, however, our information is still meagre—is to be representative of this future society, is it likely to provide anything more important than, for example, a lower-middle-class Royal Academy instead of one supplying portrait painters for aldermen?

It may be that I have wholly failed to understand what Mr Dawson is after: if so, I can only hope that he will let us have a fuller exposition of his ideas. Unless some useful analogy can be given from the past, I cannot understand the 'organization of culture', which appears to be without precedent; and in isolating culture from religion, politics and philosophy we seem to be left with something no more apprehensible than the scent of last year's roses. When we speak of culture, I suppose that we have in mind the existence of two classes of people: the producers and the consumers of culture—the existence of men who can create new thought and new art (with middlemen who can teach the consumers to like it) and the existence of a cultivated society to enjoy and patronize it. The former you can only encourage, the latter you can only educate.

I would not belittle the importance, in a period of transition, of the rearguard action; of such institutions, in their various special ways, as the National Trust, the Society for the Preservation of Ancient Buildings, even the National Society. We ought not to cut down old trees until we have learned to plant new ones. But Mr Dawson is concerned with something more important than the preservation of relics of former culture. My provisional view can only be that 'culture' is a by-product, and that those who sympathize with Mr Dawson in resenting the tyranny of politics, must direct their attention to the problem of Education, and of how, in the lower-middle-class society of the future, to provide for the training of an élite of thought, conduct and taste.

When I speak of a probable 'lower-middle-class society' I do not anticipate – short of some at present unpredictable revolution—the rise in Britain of a lower-middle-class political hierarchy, though our ruling class will have to cultivate, in its dealings with foreign countries, an understanding of that mentality. Britain will presumably continue to be governed by the same mercantile and financial class which, with a continual change of personnel, has been increasingly important since the fifteenth century. I mean by a 'lower-middle-class society' one in which the standard man legislated for and catered for, the man whose passions must be manipulated, whose prejudices must be humoured, whose tastes must be gratified, will be the lower-middle-class man. He is the most numerous, the one most necessary to flatter. I am not necessarily implying that this is either a good or a bad thing: that depends upon what lower-middle-class Man does to himself, and what is done to him.

P. 72. Advocates of Disestablishment. It is interesting to compare Bishop Hensley Henson's vigorous defence of the Establishment, *Cui Bono?*, published more than forty years ago, with his more recent *Disestablishment*, in which he took a contrary view, but too great importance could be attached, by one side or the other, to this recantation. The argument for Establishment in the early essay, and the argument against it in the later, are both well presented, and both deserve study. What has happened seems to me to be simply that Bishop Hensley Henson has come to take a different view of the tendencies of modern society; and the changes since the end of the last century are great enough to excuse such a change of opinion. His early argument is not invalidated; he might say that the situation is now such that it cannot be applied.

I must take this occasion for calling attention to the great excellence of Bishop Hensley Henson's prose, whether it is employed in a volume prepared at leisure, or in an occasional letter to *The Times*. For vigour and purity of controversial English, he has no superior today, and his writings should long continue to be studied by those who aspire to write well.

P. 74. The dangers of a nationalistic Church. Doubts about the doctrinal security of a national Church must come to the mind of any reader of Mr Middleton Murry's *The Price of Leadership*. The first part of this book I read with the warmest admiration, and I can support all that Mr Murry says in favour of a National Church against sectarianism and private Christianity. But at the point at which Mr Murry allies himself with Dr Thomas Arnold I begin to hesitate. I have no first-hand acquaintance with the doctrines of Dr Arnold, and must rely upon Mr Murry's exposition of them. But Mr Murry does not engage my complete confidence in Arnold; nor do the citations of Arnold reassure me about the orthodoxy of Mr Murry. Mr Murry holds that 'the real conflict that is preparing is the conflict between Christianity and anti-Christian nationalism': but surely a nationalism which is overtly antagonistic to Christianity is a less dangerous menace for us than a nationalism which professes a Christianity from which all Christian content has been evacuated. That the Church in England should be identical with the nation—a view which Mr Murry believes he has found in Arnold and before him in Coleridge, and which Mr Murry himself accepts—is a laudable aim so long as we keep in mind that we are speaking of one aspect of the Church; but unless this is balanced by the idea of the relation of the Church in England to the Universal Church, I see no safeguard for the purity or the catholicity of its doctrine. I am not even sure that Mr Murry desires such a safeguard. He quotes, with apparent approval, this sentence by Matthew Arnold: 'Will there never arise among Catholics some great soul, to perceive that the eternity and universality, which is vainly claimed for Catholic dogma and the ultramontane system, might really be possible for Catholic worship?'

Well! if eternity and universality is to be found, not in dogma, but in worship—that means, in a common form of worship which will mean to the worshippers anything that they like to fancy—then the result seems to me to be likely to be the most corrupt form of ritualism. What does Mr Murry mean by Christianity in his National Church, except whatever the nation as such may decide to call Christianity, and what is to prevent the Christianity from being degraded to the nationalism, rather than the nationalism being raised to Christianity?

Mr Murry holds that Dr Arnold introduced a new Christian spirit into the public schools. I would not deny to Dr Arnold the honour of having reformed and improved the moral standards inculcated by public schools, or dispute the assertion that to him and to his son 'we owe the tradition of disinterested public service.' But at what price? Mr Murry believes that the ideals of Dr Arnold have been degraded and adulterated by a subsequent generation: I would like to be sure that the results were not implicit in the principles. To me there appear to be further possible results. Mr Murry says, 'The main organ of this new national and Christian society is the state; the state is, indeed, the organ indispensable to its manifestation. For this reason it is inevitable that in the new national society, if it is to be in some real sense a Christian society, the Church and the state should draw together. On the nature of this drawing together of Church and state, everything depends.'

This paragraph, especially in conjunction with Mr Murry's suggestion that the public schools should be taken over by the state, makes me suspect that Mr Murry is ready to go a long way towards totalitarianism; and without any explicit statement on his part about the Christian beliefs which are necessary for salvation, or about the supernatural reality of the Church, we might even conclude that he would go some way in the direction of an English National Religion, the formulation of which would be taken in hand by the moral re-armament manufacturers.

Mr Murry appears (p. 111) to follow Dr Arnold in attaching little importance to the apostolical succession. With regard to the position of Matthew Arnold, he says (p. 125), 'In this situation no mere revival of Christian piety could possibly avail: not even a rebirth of Christian saintliness (such as he admired in Newman) could be efficacious against it.' It is only a short step from employing the adjective *mere* to ignoring Christian piety. He continues, 'What was required was a renovation of Christian understanding, and enlarged conception of the spiritual life itself.'

How such an enlargement of the conception of the spiritual life is to take place without spiritual masters, without the rebirth of saintliness, I cannot conceive.

P. 78. Wave of revivalism. 'Moral re-armament' has been competently and authoritatively analysed from the theological point of view by Fr. Hilary Carpenter, OP, in the April 1939 issue of *Blackfriars*, and by Professor H. A. Hodges in the May issue of *Theology*. But I feel that everything that remains of clear thinking in this country should be summoned to protest against this abuse of Christianity and of English. A reading of Mr H. W. Austin's compilation *Moral Re-Armament* suggests several lines of thought. Our immediate reflection is upon the extraordinary facility with which men of the greatest eminence will lend their names to any public appeal, however obscure or ambiguous. Another thought is that the kind of mental activity exposed by these letters must have a very demoralizing effect upon the language. Coleridge remarked that 'in a language like ours, where so many words are derived from other languages, there are few modes of instruction more useful or more amusing than that of accustoming young people to seek for the etymology, or primary meaning, of the words they use. There are cases, in which more knowledge of more value may be conveyed by the history of a word, than by the history of a campaign.' For instance, in a letter to *The Times* reprinted in Mr Austin's pamphlet, it is said that 'national security at home and abroad can only be gained through moral regeneration.' Even allowing that '*moral* regeneration' is intended to represent some milder form of parturition than *regeneration*, it is a very striking adaptation of the words of the Gospel to declare that unless a nation be born again it cannot achieve national security. The word *regeneration* appears to have degenerated. In the next paragraph 'regeneration' has been replaced by 're-armament'. I do not doubt that the term 'moral and spiritual re-armament' was originally coined merely as a striking reminder that we need something more than material equipment, but it has quickly shrunk to imply another kind of equipment *on the same plane*: that is, for ends which need be no better than worldly.

In spite of the fervour which tinges the whole correspondence, I cannot find anything to suggest that *Christianity* is needed. Some of the signers, at least, I know to be Christians, but the movement in itself, to judge by this pamphlet, is no more essentially Christian than the German National Religion of Professor Hauer. I have no first-hand experience of the Buchmanite Movement, by which this pamphlet appears to be inspired, but I have never seen any evidence that to be a Buchmanite it was necessary to hold the Christian Faith according to the Creeds, and until I have seen a statement to that effect, I shall continue to doubt whether there is any reason to call Buchmanism a Christian movement.

I am alarmed, by what are not necessary implications, but are certainly possibilities, and to my mind probabilities, of further development of this kind. It is the possibility of gradually adapting our religion to fit our secular aims—*some* of which may be worthy aims, but none of which will be criticized by a supernatural measure. Moral re-armament in my opinion may easily lead to a progressive Germanization of our society. We observe the efficiency of the German machine, and we perceive that we cannot emulate it without a kind of religious enthusiasm. Moral re-armament will provide the enthusiasm, and be the most useful kind of political drug—that is to say, having the potency at once of a stimulant and a narcotic: but it will supply this function to the detriment of our religion.

There is a tendency, especially among the English-speaking Protestant peoples, to treat religion as a kind of social tonic that can be used in times of national emergency in order to extract a further degree of moral effort from the people. But apart from the Pelagian conception of religion that this view implies, it is not wholly sound from the psychological point of view, since it merely heightens the amount of moral tension without increasing the sources of spiritual vitality or resolving the psychological conflicts from which the society suffers.

Christopher Dawson: *Beyond Politics,* p. 21.

While the humanistic religious sentiment which expresses itself by the catch in the throat at the last Evensong in the old School Chapel, the community singing of *Abide with me* at a torchlight tattoo, and the standing to attention during the Two Minutes' Silence, can be utilized by totalitarianism, a religion which speaks of redemption by the incarnate Son of God, which offers mankind the sacramental means of union with the eternal life of the God-Man Jesus Christ, and which makes the perpetual representation of His atoning Sacrifice its essential act of worship must be the declared enemy of all who see in the state the be-all and end-all of man's life.

Humphrey Beevor: Peace and Pacifism, p. 207.

P. 83. I have permission to reprint, fron *The Times* of 5 October 1938, the following letter, which might serve either as prologue or epilogue to all that I have said, and which provided the immediate stimulus for the lectures which form this book.

3 October 1938.

Sir,

The lessons which are being drawn from the unforgettable experiences through which we have lived during the past few days do not for the most part seem to me to go deep enough. The period of grace that has been given us may be no more than a postponement of the day of reckoning unless we make up our minds to seek a radical cure. Our civilization can recover only if we are determined to root out the cancerous growths which have brought it to the verge of complete collapse. Whether truth and justice or caprice and violence are to prevail in human affairs is a question on which the fate of mankind depends. But to equate the conflict between these opposing forces with the contrast between democracies and dictatorships, real and profound as is this difference, is a dangerous simplification of the problem. To focus our attention on evil in others is a way of escape from the painful struggle of eradicating it from our own hearts and lives and an evasion of our real responsibilities.

The basal truth is that the spiritual foundations of western civilization have been undermined. The systems which are in the ascendant on the continent may be regarded from one point of view as convulsive attempts to arrest the process of disintegration. What clear alternative have we in this country? The mind of England is confused and uncertain. Is it possible that a simple question, an affirmative answer to which is for many a matter of course and for many others an idle dream or sheer lunacy, might in these circumstances become a live and serious issue? May our salvation lie in an attempt to recover our Christian heritage, not in the sense of going back to the past but of discovering in the central affirmations and insights of the Christian faith new spiritual energies to regenerate and vitalize our sick society? Does not the public repudiation of the whole Christian scheme of life in a large part of what was once known as Christendom force to the front the question whether the path of wisdom is not rather to attempt to work out a Christian doctrine of modern society and to order our national life in accordance with it?

Those who would give a quick, easy or confident answer to this question have failed to understand it. It cannot even be seriously considered without a profound awareness of the extent to which Christian ideas have lost their hold over, or faded from the consciousness of, large sections of the population; of the far-reaching changes that would be called for in the structure, institutions and activities of existing society, which is in many of its features a complete denial of the Christian understanding of the meaning and end of man's existence; and of the stupendous and costly spiritual, moral and intellectual effort that any genuine attempt to order the national life in accordance with the Christian understanding of life would demand. Realistically viewed the task is so far beyond the present capacity of our British Christianity that I write as a fool. But if the will were there, I believe that the first steps to be taken are fairly clear. The presupposition of all else, however, is the recognition that nothing short of a really heroic effort will avail to save mankind from its present evils and the destruction which must follow in their train.

I am, Sir,

Yours etc.

(Signed) J. H. OLDHAM

POSTSCRIPT

A distinguished theologian, who has been so kind as to read the proofs of this book, has made criticisms of which I should have liked to avail myself by a thorough revision of the text. He has allowed me to quote the following passage from his criticism, which the reader may find helpful in correcting some of the defects of my presentation:

> The main theses of this book seem to me so important, and their application so urgently necessary, that I want to call attention to two points which I think need further emphasis, lest the point of the argument should be missed.
>
> A main part of the problem, as regards the actual Church and its existing members, is the defective realization among us of the fundamental fact that Christianity is primarily a Gospel-message, a dogma, a belief about God and the world and man, which demands of man a response of faith and repentance. The common failure lies in putting the human response first, and so thinking of Christianity as primarily a *religion*. Consequently there is among us a tendency to view the problems of the day in the light of what is practically possible, rather than in the light of what is imposed by the principles of that truth to which the Church is set to bear witness.
>
> Secondly, there is a general vagueness about 'the Community of Christians'. I fear the phrase will be interpreted to mean nice Christianly-minded people of the upper middle class (p. 80). But the Community of Christians ought to mean those who are gathered into unity in the sacramental life of the visible Church: and this community in the life of faith ought to be producing something of a common mind about the questions of the day. It cannot indeed be assumed that the mind of the Community of Christians is truly reflected in the ecclesiastical pronouncements which from time to time appear: that mind does not form itself quickly, in these matters

in which it is so hard to see the way. There ought however to be, and to some real extent there is now, in the minds of Christian people a sense of the proportion of things and a spirit of discipline, which are direct fruits of the life of faith: and it is these that need to be brought to bear if the questions are to be answered in the light of Christian principles.

APPENDIX

The following broadcast talk, delivered in February 1937 in a series on 'Church, Community and State', and printed in the Listener, *has some relevance to the matter of the preceding pages of this book.*

That there is an antithesis between the Church and the World is a belief we derive from the highest authority. We know also from our reading of history, that a certain tension between Church and State is desirable. When Church and State fall out completely, it is ill with the commonwealth; and when Church and State get on too well together, there is something wrong with the Church. But the distinction between the Church and the World is not so easy to draw as that between Church and State. Here we mean not any one communion or ecclesiastical organization but the whole number of Christians as Christians; and we mean not any particular State, but the whole of society, the world over, in its secular aspect. The antithesis is not simply between two opposed groups of individuals: every individual is himself a field in which the forces of the Church and the world struggle.

By 'the Church's message to the World' you might think that what was meant was only the business of the Church to go on talking. I should like to make it more urgent by expanding the title to 'the Church's business to interfere with the World'. What is often assumed, and it is a principle that I wish to oppose, is the principle of live-and-let-live. It is assumed that if the State leaves the Church alone, and to some extent protects it from molestation, then the Church has no right to interfere with the organization of society, or with the conduct of those who deny its beliefs. It is assumed that any such interference would be the oppression of the majority by a minority. Christians must take a very different view of their duty. But before suggesting *how* the Church should interfere with the World, we must try to answer the question: *why* should it interfere with the World?

It must be said bluntly that between the Church and the World there is no permanent *modus vivendi* possible. We may unconsciously draw a false analogy between the position of the Church in a secular society and the position of a dissenting sect in a Christian society. The situation is very different. A dissenting minority in a Christian society can persist because of the fundamental beliefs it has in common with that society, because of a common morality and of common grounds of Christian action. Where there is a different morality there is conflict. I do not mean that the Church exists primarily for the propagation of Christian morality: morality is a means and not an end. The Church exists for the glory of God and the sanctification of souls: Christian morality is part of the means by which these ends are to be attained. But because Christian morals are based on fixed beliefs which cannot change they also are essentially unchanging: while the beliefs and in consequence the morality of the secular world can change from individual to individual, or from generation to generation, or from nation to nation. To accept two ways of life in the same society, one for the Christian and another for the rest would be for the Church to abandon its task of evangelizing the world. For the more alien the non-Christian world becomes, the more difficult becomes its conversion.

The Church is not merely for the elect—in other words, those whose temperament brings them to that belief and that behaviour. Nor does it allow us to be Christian in some social relations and non-Christian in others. It wants everybody, and it wants each individual as a whole. It therefore must struggle for a condition of society which will give the maximum of opportunity for us to lead wholly Christian lives, and the maximum of opportunity for others to become Christians. It maintains the paradox that while we are each responsible for our own souls, we are all responsible for all other souls, who are, like us, on their way to a future state of heaven or hell. And—another paradox—as the Christian attitude towards peace, happiness and well-being of peoples is that they are a means and not an end in themselves, Christians are more deeply committed to realizing these ideals than are those who regard them as ends in themselves.

Now, *how* is the Church to interfere in the World? I do not propose to take up the rest of my time by denouncing Fascism and Communism. This task has been more ably performed by others, and the conclusions may be taken for granted. By pursuing this charge, I might obtain from you a kind of approval that I do not want. I suspect that a good deal of the dislike of these philosophies in this country is due to the wrong reasons as well as the right, and is coloured with complacency and sanctimony. It is easy, safe and pleasant to criticize foreigners; and it has the advantage of distracting attention from the evils of our own society. We must distinguish also between our opposition to *ideas* and our disapproval of *practices*. Both Fascism and Communism have fundamental ideas which are incompatible with Christianity. But in practice, a Fascist or a Communist State might realize its idea more or less, and it might be more or less tolerable. And on the other hand, the practices, or others equally objectionable, might easily intrude themselves into a society nominally attached to quite different principles. We need not assume that our form of constitutional democracy is the only one suitable for a Christian people, or that it is in itself a guarantee against an anti-Christian world. Instead of merely condemning Fascism and Communism, therefore, we might do well to consider that we also live in a mass-civilization following many wrong ambitions and wrong desires, and that if our society renounces completely its obedience to God, it will become no better, and possibly worse, than some of those abroad which are popularly execrated.

By 'the world', then, I mean for my present purpose particularly the world in this island. The influence of the Church can be exerted in several ways. It may oppose, or it may support, particular actions at particular times. It is acclaimed when it supports any cause that is already assured of a good deal of secular support: it is attacked, quite naturally, when it opposes anything that people think they want. Whether people say that the Church ought to interfere, or whether they say it ought to mind its own business, depends mostly on whether they agree or disagree with its attitude upon the issue of the moment. A very difficult problem arises whenever there is occasion for the Church to resist any innovation—either in legislation or in social practice—which is contrary to Christian principles. To those who deny, or do not fully accept, Christian doctrine, or who wish to interpret it according to their private lights, such resistance often appears oppressive. To the unreasoning mind the Church can often be made to appear to be the enemy of progress and enlightenment. The Church may not always be strong enough to resist successfully: but I do not see how it can ever accept as a permanent settlement one law for itself and another for the world.

I do not wish, however, to pursue the question of the kinds of issue which may arise from time to time. I want to suggest that a task for the Church in our age is a more profound scrutiny of our society, which shall start from the question: to what depth is the foundation of our society not merely neutral but positively anti-Christian?

It ought not to be necessary for me to insist that the final aims of the churchman, and the aims of the secular reformer, are very different. So far as the aims of the latter are for true social justice, they ought to be comprehended in those of the former. But one reason why the lot of the secular reformer or revolutionist seems to me to be the easier is this: that for the most part he conceives of the evils of the world as something external to himself. They are thought of either as completely impersonal, so that there is nothing to alter but machinery; or if there is evil *incarnate*, it is always incarnate in the *other people*—a class, a race, the politicians, the bankers, the armament makers, and so forth—never in oneself. There are individual exceptions: but so far as a man sees the need for converting *himself* as well as the World, he is approximating to the religious point of view. But for most people, to be able to simplify issues so as to see only the definite external enemy, is extremely exhilarating, and brings about the bright eye and the springy step that go so well with the political uniform. This is an exhilaration that the Christian must deny himself. It comes from an artificial stimulant bound to have bad after-effects. It causes pride, either individual or collective, and pride brings its own doom. For only in humility, charity and purity—and most of all perhaps humility—can we be prepared to receive the grace of God without which human operations are vain.

It is not enough simply to see the evil and injustice and suffering of this world, and precipitate oneself into action. We must know, what only theology can tell us, why these things are wrong. Otherwise, we may right some wrongs at the cost of creating new ones. If this is a world in which I, and the majority of my fellow-beings, live in that perpetual distraction from God which exposes us to the one great peril, that of final and complete alienation from God after death, there is some wrong that I must try to help to put right. If there is any profound immorality to which we are all committed as a condition of living in society at all, that is a matter of the gravest concern to the Church. I am neither a sociologist nor an economist, and in any case it would be inappropriate, in this context, to produce any formula for setting the world right. It is much more the business of the Church to say what is wrong, that is, what is inconsistent with Christian doctrine, than to propose particular schemes of improvement. What is right enters the realm of the *expedient* and is contingent upon place and time, the degree of culture, the temperament of a people. But the Church can say what is always and everywhere *wrong*. And without this firm assurance of first principles which it is the business of the Church to repeat in and out of season, the World will constantly confuse the *right* with the expedient. In a society based on the use of slave labour men tried to prove from the Bible that slavery was something ordained by God. For most people, the actual constitution of Society, or that which their more generous passions wish to bring about, is right, and Christianity must be adapted to it. But the Church cannot be, in any political sense, either conservative, or liberal, or revolutionary. Conservatism is too often conservation of the wrong things; liberalism a relaxation of discipline; revolution a denial of the permanent things.

Perhaps the dominant vice of our time, from the point of view of the Church, will be proved to be Avarice. Surely there is something wrong in our attitude towards money. The acquisitive, rather than the creative and spiritual instincts, are encouraged. The fact that money is always forthcoming for the purpose of making more money, whilst it is so difficult to obtain for purposes of exchange, and for the needs of the most needy, is disturbing to those who are not economists. I am by no means sure that it is right for me to improve any income by investing in the shares of a company, making I know not what, operating perhaps thousands of miles away, and in the control of which I have no effective voice—but which is recommended as a sound investment. I am still less sure of the morality of my being a moneylender: that is, of investing in bonds and debentures. I know that it is wrong for me to speculate: but where the line is to be drawn between speculation and what is called legitimate investment is by no means clear. I seem to be a petty usurer in a world manipulated largely by big usurers. And I know that the Church once condemned these things. And I believe that modern war is chiefly caused by some immorality of competition which is always with us in times of 'peace'; and that until this evil is cured, no leagues or disarmaments or collective security or conferences or conventions or treaties will suffice to prevent it.

Any machinery, however beautiful to look at and however wonderful a product of brains and skill, can be used for bad purposes as well as good: and this is as true of social machinery as of constructions of steel. I think that, more important than the invention of a new machine, is the creation of a temper of mind in people such that they can learn to use a new machine rightly. More important still at the moment would be the diffusion of knowledge of what is wrong—*morally* wrong—and of *why* it is wrong. We are all dissatisfied with the way in which the world is conducted: some believe that it is a misconduct in which we all have some complicity; some believe that if we trust ourselves entirely to politics, sociology or economics we shall only shuffle from one makeshift to another. And here is the perpetual message of the Church: to affirm, to teach and to apply, true theology. We cannot be satisfied to be Christians at our devotions and merely secular reformers all the rest of the week, for there is one question that we need to ask ourselves every day and about whatever business. The Church has perpetually to answer this question: to what purpose were we born? What is the end of Man?

A Sub-Christian Society?

A review by Maurice B. Reckitt in the *New English Weekly*, 7 December 1939

I CANNOT resist the feeling of a certain unreality attaching to the attempt to review this book. For reviews are commonly, and not altogether unjustifiably, regarded as a means of conveying—or alternatively of obtaining—the gist of a book as a preliminary to (or more often as a substitute for) the reading of it. But Mr Eliot's book is so short, so succinct, and written with such a crystalline brilliance (Dr Keith Feiling has well spoken of 'the severe impact of its phrasing') that no one who is even remotely interested either in Mr Eliot or in his subject will fail to read it for themselves, and no one is likely to be particularly interested to know what may be anyone else's opinion about it. The reader will be in too much of a hurry to take the obvious course of forming his own. In any case, the book has been widely reviewed and thoroughly summarized in the press already, and those who have anything interesting to say about it have probably said it by this time. I particularly commend Canon Charles Smyth's notice in the *Spectator*, which also, however, embarrasses me somewhat by saying exactly what I should have wished to say a good deal better than I could say it.

What I have not seen generally pointed out is that this book is not the product of any purely theoretical interest in the subject; it is the response to a shock. Mr Eliot confesses himself to have been 'deeply shaken by the events of September, 1938, in a way from which one does not recover', and to be one (as he suspects) of many who experienced a 'new and unexpected feeling of humiliation, which seemed to demand an act of personal contrition, of humility, repentance and amendment; what had happened was something in which one was deeply implicated and responsible', something which suggested 'doubt of the validity of a civilization. We could not match conviction with conviction.' This strongly personal and even emotional statement, the mood of which is reproduced in the admirable letter of Dr J. H. Oldham written to *The Times* on the occasion itself, reprinted at the end of Mr Eliot's notes, and which provided, as he says, the 'immediate stimulus' for these lectures, is interesting for two reasons. First, because it provides an excellent expression of ideas (or more precisely, facts) to which many people find it hard to attach any meaning—corporate sin and corporate penitence. And secondly, because Mr Eliot reacted to this experience not, as do most of us if we ever attain to such experiences, by feeling and lamenting, but by thinking. This book is that rare phenomenon in English life—the response to a moral challenge of a Christian mind.

I shall not attempt to praise Mr Eliot's book, for that would be impertinent, nor to summarize it, for (as the first paragraph of this review suggests) that would be superfluous. Mr Eliot himself describes it as 'a discussion which must occupy many minds for a long time', and no review could possibly follow up all the clues which are here suggested. Have we got a Christian society—whatever that may be? No, says Mr Eliot, we have a neutral one, and its difference in idea from a pagan one 'is, in the long run, of minor importance', but, he goes on to insist, 'a society has not ceased to be Christian until it has become positively something else', and though our culture is mainly negative, 'so far as it is positive, it is still Christian'. But the situation is much more serious than the average Christian realizes, 'as the problem is constituted by our implication in a network of institutions from which we cannot dissociate ourselves: institutions the operation of which appears no longer neutral, but non-Christian.' The ordinary man who believes himself in some real sense a Christian is in fact 'becoming more and more de-Christianized by all sorts of unconscious pressure; paganism holds all the most valuable advertising space. Anything like Christian traditions transmitted from generation to generation within the family must disappear, and the small body of Christians will consist entirely of adult recruits' who have rediscovered the Faith for themselves. Even if quality thus compensates for quantity (an undoubted tendency, which nevertheless Mr Eliot seems to me to exaggerate), obviously the prospects are far from bright for the transition from a neutral to a Christian society—whatever that may be.

Though Mr Eliot says 'I am very much concerned with making clear its difference from the kind of society in which we are now living', he has not very much that is specific to say about this, and the divergence of our present order from a Christian one is a matter not discussed in any detail. We do, however, get a definition of a Christian society which 'would be one in which the natural end of man—virtue and well-being in community—is acknowledged for all, and the supernatural end—beatitude—for those who have eyes to see it'. Now here, assuredly, might start 'a discussion which must occupy many minds for a long time', and indeed I think it should, for at this central point emerges perhaps the most disputable issue in the book, and one which creates so much difficulty for me that I must devote the rest of my space to it. For though I entirely agree with Mr Eliot that 'a wrong attitude towards nature implies, somewhere, a wrong attitude towards God', I am unable to see how the acceptance of a 'natural end' by those whom our author (as he shows elsewhere) clearly regards as the great majority of any foreseeable order, can create a Christian society. It seems to me to suggest far more definitely a pagan society, if that word were used in its accurate connotation, and not as Mr Eliot, following what I think is a convention unworthy of his precise diction, uses it to indicate the demonic orders of the modern world.

So many summaries of this book have appeared that probably all my readers will know that Mr Eliot distinguishes 'the Christian State, the Christian Community and the Community of Christians', as elements of the Christian Society. I do not think these titles altogether happily chosen, but there is no difficulty in understanding what Mr Eliot is seeking to distinguish, and the distinction is very suggestive of the elements of medieval Christendom, if we take as parallels the ruling caste, the mass of the population, and the religious orders. A hundred years ago Coleridge had an analogous category to the last-named in mind when he coined the term 'clerisy', but Mr Eliot gives good reasons for thinking that this term—at any rate in Coleridge's sense, and it is not much good using it in any other—should be discarded. Mr Eliot admits he has in mind 'a body of nebulous outline'—those of 'superior intellectual and/or spiritual gifts' who accept a cultural responsibility on an explicitly Christian basis, and from whom 'one could expect a conscious Christian life on its highest social level'. From the rulers of the Christian State Mr Eliot would exact only a 'conscious conformity' and such a degree of Christian education (the content of which he does not discuss) as would enable them 'to think in Christian categories', for as he very sensibly points out, 'it is the general ethics of the people they have to govern, not their own piety, that determines the behaviour of politicians.'

But it is when we come to the great mass of the 'Christian Community' that the question which troubles me arises. When Mr Eliot says that 'their religious and social life should form for them a natural whole so that the difficulty of behaving as Christians should not impose [on them] an intolerable strain', he is only re-affirming the very important truth stated by M. Maritain more than ten years ago, that it is the business of a social order to make the world not holy (which no social order can be) but 'habitable', so that a man is not 'obliged to heroism', to live a Christian life in it. And it is relevant to this point to add, as Mr Eliot does, that 'behaviour is as potent to affect belief, as belief to affect behaviour'; hence an order in which the majority can lead a life congruous with Christian values is of importance not only for its inherent validity, but on account of the support it gives to the Faith on which ultimately those values depend.

But Mr Eliot goes further than this. He says [my italics] 'the *religious life* of the people would be *largely* a matter of behaviour and conformity'; and again, he envisages 'a community of men and women; *not individually better* than they are now, *except* for the capital difference of holding the Christian faith'. One is forced to the question what relation a 'religious life' of this quality bears to the religion of the New Testament. No doubt the language of the Epistles—'called to be saints', 'the measure of the stature of the fulness of Christ'—was addressed to 'Christian communities' in a situation vastly different from the Christianity community Mr Eliot envisages. But a religion which expects no more than this, nothing more elevated, nothing more heroic, from the mass of its devotees can surely be little more than an official cult and a code of morals. 'Social customs', says Mr Eliot, 'would take on religious sanctions.' But if this is all that happens, the new Christendom will be likely to repeat those errors of the old which led to so much evil and contributed to the apostasy of Europe by the nourishing of superstition within the ecclesiastical integument, and by a readiness to treat religion as instrumental to social ends. The 'moral revivalism' which Mr Eliot sees as our national weakness, and the inadequacy of which he so effectively exposes, is merely the recurrent reaction which inevitably waits upon any religion which is content to be regarded as 'largely a matter of behaviour and conformity'; and there are some among the warmest of Mr Eliot's admirers for whom this represents no true idea of a Christian society.

A reply by T. S. Eliot in the *New English Weekly*, 14 December 1939

Mr Maurice Reckitt, in his kindly review of my book in the last issue, raises a point which is of considerable interest in itself. That the point is raised does not surprise me; but I am a little surprised by the criticism coming from this quarter—coming from which I am compelled to give it the most careful consideration. Nevertheless, I do not write as one having the slightest ground of complaint, but in gratitude to a reviewer who has done what is rare: raised a point which is relevant but which greatly transcends in importance the book itself.

Mr Reckitt expresses, by the title of his article, the suspicion that the society which I have outlined would not be Christian but sub-Christian. There are here two questions which should not be confused: the question of a criticism of my nomenclature, and the question whether the 'Christian Society' of my book is too poor an ideal to be worth keeping before us. The first question cannot wholly be neglected, but it has little importance except in relation to the second. For the first question, I have consulted the OED for the definition of 'pagan', and it seems to confirm my belief that my use of the word is at least as justifiable as Mr Reckitt's. To him, a 'pagan society' seems to mean one in which only material values, or material *and* inter-personal values on the human plane, are recognized; to me, a 'pagan society' is one in which the wrong spiritual values are recognized.

The centre of the difference, however, is elsewhere; and I should like to assure myself first that Mr Reckitt—in spite of, or perhaps because of, my laborious attempts to make clear the limitations which I imposed upon myself—has in no respect misunderstood me. He quotes me as defining a Christian society as one 'in which the natural end of man—virtue and well-being in community—is acknowledged for all, and the supernatural end—beatitude—for those who have eyes to see it'. Now in order to explain what I meant by this I had better go back to the source of the phrasing. It is a book by one Marcel Demongeot, called *Le meilleur régime politique selon Saint Thomas*: I am indebted to the author directly and also to his quotations from the master.

De. Reg. I, 14: Videtur autem finis esse multitudinis congregatae vivere secundum virtutem. Ad hoc enim homines congregantur, ut simul bene vivant ... bona autem vita est secundum virtutem, virtuosa igitur vita est congregationis humanae finis.

The author says a little later:

> Aristote bornait en effet le bien commun à une vie intérieure purement terrestre, si élevée fût-elle; saint Thomas christianise, en la reprenant, la pensée d'Aristote; sans faire de la vie éternelle la fin propre et directe de la cité, il considère que la vie vertueuse qui en est la fin ne saurait avoir le caractère de fin dernière, mais doit s'orienter elle-même vers la béatitude parfaite; la cité doit au moins créer les conditions sociales qui permettront le mieux à ses membres de gagner le ciel. 'Non est ergo ultimus finis multitudinis congregatae vivere secundum virtutem, sed per virtuosam vitam pervenire ad fruitionem divinam' (*De. Reg.* I, 14).

Mr Reckitt will at this point be about to exclaim that I have added a little bit of my own to this conception of the City: so I hasten to admit it at once. What I have added is simply the admission, that my City must find a place for inhabitants who fail to recognize the Christian revelation. But if my society is to be a Christian Society, this part of the population must be a minority. Is it possible that in reading my sentence, Mr Reckitt has taken *all* to correspond to 'the Christian Community', and *those who have eyes to see it* to correspond to 'the Community of Christians'? That is not what I meant: I intended that even the intellectually least developed should, with however bleared a vision, acknowledge the supernatural end of beatitude.

Mr Reckitt tells us that he is 'unable to see how the acceptance of a "natural end" by those whom our author [as he shows elsewhere] clearly regards as the great majority of any forseeable order, can create a Christian Society'. On this point, we are certainly in agreement, though Mr Reckitt seems not to think so. For if Mr Reckitt infers that I believe that the acceptance of a natural end by the great majority can create a Christian society, he obviously thinks that I have fallen into the grossest heresy. I do not believe that Christianity germinates out of natural religion, but that it is given by revelation; and it is only from the Christian point of view that the 'natural ends' can be recognized as merely natural.

Even, however, if what seems to me a misunderstanding is put aside, there is still a difficulty. Concerning what I have called 'the religious life of the people', Mr Reckitt observes: 'One is forced to the question what relation a "religious life" of this quality bears to the religion of the New Testament. . . . A religion which expects no more than this, nothing more elevated, nothing more heroic, from the mass of its devotees can surely be little more than an official cult and a code of morals.' I hope that when Mr Reckitt says *expects*, he means *expects*, and not *asks*. A religion should certainly ask more than this, but if it expects more than this, it is likely to be deceived. And when we look at what the Christian Faith has meant and means, to the mass of the people—at least, in Catholic countries—I do not think that it is or has ever been merely 'an official cult and a code of morals'. As for the question what relation a religious life of this quality bears to the religion of the New Testament, it is no more than the question what relation Christendom has ever borne to the religion of the New Testament. And when I say 'Christendom', I mean the people whom St Paul reproached and admonished, as well as the populations of Europe in the Middle Ages or in our own times. Mr Reckitt's objection appears to be, that I do not expect as much of my Christian Community as I do of my Community of Christians. There is a fundamental dilemma from which it is no more possible for Mr Reckitt to escape than for me. If you design your Christian Society only according to what your experience of human beings, and the history of the last nineteen hundred years, tells you is possible, then it must remain open to the charge of being sub-Christian. If you design it beyond experience and history, you are committed to utopian plans the impracticality of which will expose you to relapse into a Lutheran despair of this world. I do not deny the possibility of a much more Christian society than that which I have outlined: for all things are possible to God. And I am aware that one cannot hold any view on these matters except in imminent peril of falling into one heresy or another: if I risk destruction in Pelagianism, Mr Reckitt the theologian runs the danger of abandoning the world to Mr Reckitt the social worker. Mr Reckitt seems to suppose that he has condemned my Christian Society by suggesting that it 'will be likely to repeat those errors of the old which have led to so much evil and contributed to the apostasy of Europe by the nourishing of superstition within the ecclesiastical integument, and by a readiness to treat religion as instrumental to social ends'. But of course! It will be likely to repeat every error of the past: I did not attempt to sketch anything but a human society—that is to say, a society which, whatever spiritual heights it reaches, is liable always and at any moment to fall out of the hand of God.

A letter from T. S. Eliot to the Editor of the *New English Weekly*, 1 February 1940

When, as Mr Reckitt reminds me, I 'welcomed the possibility of a discussion which must occupy many minds for a long time', I did *not* mean that I hoped that people would continue to discuss my book for a long time; and I write now, not for the purpose of provoking a fresh burst of correspondence, but to make a few observations in retrospect.

I am grateful to Mr Reckitt for drawing attention to more than one obscurity in my phrasing. It is always possible that a statement which is misunderstood in different ways by everybody, may still be the only way in which the thought could be put: but any statement which is misunderstood in the same way by different people is one that ought to be re-framed. I therefore agree that my sentence about the natural and supernatural end of man should be re-written, now that Mr Reckitt seems to understand what I meant (or rather, what I did not mean) by it. In his letter in your issue of 18 January, Mr Reckitt cites two more sentences which must be blue-pencilled.

It should by now be clear that I was trying to limit myself to the *minimal* requirements in a society before it could be *called* a Christian society; and that I should not necessarily be satisfied with what I had outlined. It was, perhaps, misleading to speak of a 'community of men and women, not individually better than they are now', since I was unable to make clear that the real gulf to be bridged, from the point of view taken up throughout the essay, was not that between the spiritually backward and the spiritually advanced individual, but between one and another kind of collective attitude. The difficulty about my other sentence, 'Social customs would take on religious sanctions' is of another sort. I was only attempting to suggest what I thought was sure to happen in my society, not what I advocated and approved; and I did indicate elsewhere that it would be the business of the Church—primarily in the sense of the hierarchy—to check such identifications from going too far.

I did not mean to imply, anywhere, that any Christian, by reason of being engaged in manual labour, or on any other ground, was 'absolved' from the obligation of prayer and self-improvement in the spiritual life. I repeat, I was concerned with minimal requirements. If you say that my requirements were so modest that the result—however superior to our present situation—would not produce anything that could justifiably be called a 'Christian society', I can only say that I think you must abandon altogether the hope for a Christian society, and limit your thinking to the possibilities of a Christian community within a non-Christian one.

I am not obstinately attached to the term 'pagan', as the alternative to 'Christian'. I shall be glad if anyone can tell me of a better: I wanted to avoid, as far as I could, using (or rather abusing) the term 'secular'.

Towards a Christian Britain

A talk broadcast by the BBC in a series on *The Church Looks Ahead* and printed in the *Listener*, 10 April 1941

AT the point at which I enter this discussion, I am able to take for granted that a Christian Britain is desirable. But to agree that something is desirable is not the same thing as desiring it; and if we are seriously to entertain the idea of a Christian Britain, we might as well consider in advance what an extraordinary aim this is, and how different from any of the kinds of reform or revolution that men commonly undertake. In the first place, it is unlikely that any of us, if we were presently translated to this Christian Britain, would find ourselves perfectly at home in it. It is something which demands an inner change of the individual as well as an outer change of society. I can, of course, imagine quite a different and much pleasanter society from that in which I live, so long as I assume that I shall be the same Tom, Dick, or Harry in it. I know that I should have to be different too; but to see this changed myself at all clearly is beyond the scope of imagination. We must recognize that a Christian Britain demands sacrifice from all—sacrifice of mean, petty, and selfish desires; and that what we stand to gain by it is not merely something that we now desire, but a change and perfection of our present desire and will.

Beside this thought, there is a question I should like to put to you for consideration after you have heard me out. The question to which I am to speak is: what can we do to help to bring about a Christian Britain? The question I put to you is: what sort of an answer do you expect? If you do not consider what is possible, you will not know what to ask for, and you will be dissatisfied with whatever I say. If I propose certain definite things that we can do, they will probably seem to you quite inadequate to the magnitude of the task: if I try to avoid this kind of anti-climax, I may leave you with the feeling that I have uttered only amiable platitudes which have got us nowhere. I do not want merely to offer some scheme of worldly reform which would have no need of Christianity to make it appear desirable. And I do not want to talk that language of spiritual aspiration which is nothing but words. But if you see that I have to try to avoid both of these pitfalls, you will make things easier for me.

The simplest way to begin, I think, is this. We recognize three kinds of Christian duty: duty towards God, duty towards one's neighbour, and duty towards oneself. The first can be represented by worship, the second by the effort for social justice, and the third by personal and private morality. But we have only to think for a moment to realize that each kind of duty implies, and in a sense comprehends, the others, and that none is wholly itself unless it is the others too. We are not doing our duty towards God if we are indifferent to social injustice, or if we neglect our own moral and spiritual development; we cannot truly cultivate our own moral and spiritual nature and remain indifferent to God and to our fellow men; and finally, we cannot build a Christian social order if we neglect worship or belittle the duty of self-improvement. This is obvious: but in point of fact we always tend to emphasize one duty to the neglect of others, and from this lopsidedness many of our troubles spring.

During the second part of the nineteenth century and the earlier part of this, a great deal was written urging social reform, and a good deal of action was taken. People tended to think that the problems of this world could all be solved in terms of this world—except when they supinely assumed that God did not mean us to solve them at all. And as for the Christian faith, its demands appeared to most people to be satisfied by certain observances: by the code of morals of respectable people, churchgoing, charitable contributions, perhaps family prayers. But politics was politics, and business was business. Nowadays we take the point of view that we are, each and all of us, somehow responsible for the kind of society in which we live. Hence, alongside of numerous secular schemes for putting the world right, there has grown up a considerable body of Christian criticism of our inherited social and economic order, and a widespread feeling of Christian responsibility in matters of social justice.

This new emphasis was very necessary; but we have to keep in mind that we shall never realize our Christian social aims if we cultivate them in forgetfulness of our duty towards God and our duty towards ourselves. The old-fashioned family prayers type of Christian life is now unpopular, and was often perfunctory and unattractive: but it insisted upon the important truth that Christian life begins in the family. It was usually defective in two ways: first, in teaching morality as an end in itself, or as a set of prohibitions, instead of as a necessary condition of the progress towards spiritual perfection which is the Christian goal. Second, in failing to lead the way to Christian thinking: in assuming that faith was something to be preserved, if possible, from child-hood, rather than something to be developed throughout matur-ity. It sounds as if I was asking a great deal of Christian parents: but it seems excessive because we now tend to expect too much of the schoolmaster. And there is one essential for a Christian start in life which the home, and the home only, can provide: the influence of a Christian atmosphere from the earliest years. Children are more influenced by what their parents are, than by what their parents tell them to be. So the first thing is not that parents should teach their children Christianity, but that they should be Christian parents.

Now, I have mentioned 'Christian thinking', and I want to explain what I mean. Consider the five points recently put forward by His Holiness the Pope, and the supplementary five points of the Archbishops, the Cardinal-Archbishop, and the Moderator. As nearly everyone can accept them, we are apt to overlook the possibility of our giving them different interpreta-tions, and accepting them only on our own terms. It will make a vast difference how much phrases like 'the laws of God', 'divine vocation', and 'God's gifts to the whole world' happen to mean to you. The full meaning is tremendous. But if they come to you like familiar quotations, as something which you need make no fresh effort to understand, they will probably be lost on you. This is one instance of what I mean by the necessity for Christian thinking. I mean thinking as Christians. We need to know what it is that we profess to believe, and without believing which we are not Christian. We must know the dogmas of our faith—and if you do not know what a dogma is, or why it is vitally important, then the first thing that you can do to help towards a Christian Britain is to find out. For otherwise your social thinking is not likely to be particularly Christian. Christian feeling is not enough. But itself, it may lead us to suppose that we do our social duty if we support any scheme of reform which appears to have humane and generous aims. Or it may lead us to assume that any programme elaborated by Christians is necessarily a Christian programme. Our so-called Christian programme may be merely a secular programme warmed by the glow of Christian sentiment—or perhaps only illuminated by the chilly light of Christian phrases.

Now there are certain principles of Christian conduct, of social as well as private morality, laws of right and wrong for people in authority and for people in subordination; laws of right and wrong for governments as well as for individuals. These principles are true for the Christian at all times and in all places and for all peoples. Some of these are set forth in encyclical letters of Leo XIII and Pius XI which are essential texts for Christian social thinkers of all denominations. It has often been observed, however, that principles of such universal validity usually tell us more clearly what is wrong than how to put them right. This is in the nature of things. There is a much greater measure of agreement among Christian social thinkers of different nations than you would expect to find; and if any people was prepared to take seriously what such men have said, it would lead to very profound social changes. But just as every one of us has to make his own decisions in his private life, so each nation has to make its own: and what is good for one is not always good for another. Even apart from human frailty, we cannot expect individuals or nations who are different to behave in exactly the same way: we must respect their differences as well as their likeness to each other as sons of God. But there is another problem about social reform, which we must keep always in mind. Cooperation between Christians and non-Christians is not only possible, it is necessary. But here is where our Christian thinking comes in: we must try to be clear what it is that we are cooperating for, and just where our difference matters and where it does not. We must not confuse the absolute with the relative good: we must remember that we hold a different view of human nature from the non-Christian, and that we have a different conception of the destiny of man. We must cooperate but not surrender. We must remind ourselves that there is no short cut to a Christian Britain.

This leads me to my last point. I have spoken of our duty to God, our duty to our neighbours, and our duty towards ourselves. There is also our duty towards Nature, but for my present purpose that can be comprehended in our duty towards God. I have said that we cannot perform one of these duties properly without performing the others. If our effort is one-sided, we may, on the one hand, succeed in increasing the number of Christians in Britain, and on the other we may create a Britain in which it is more possible for people to be Christian. But a Christian Britain needs more than that. And even if we set ourselves to perform all our Christian duty, there is still something lacking from our picture. I have so far spoken only of the aspect of human will, and certainly unless we seek we shall not find. But we must not forget God, without whom we can do nothing of worth, but with whom we can do everything. It is impossible to make a blue-print of a Christian order, because we cannot fit God into a blue-print. An earlier speaker has reminded us of the failure of modern man to make a success of his world without God; the converse is to remind ourselves of what we might do in reliance upon His sustaining power and in seeking to learn His will. Human effort alone can only produce a lifeless observance of rules of individual and communal devotion, and in society a Christian framework without a Christian content. We must be sure that we are relying on God, and not merely clothing still one more ambitious human scheme in the vestments of Christianity. Without humility, submission, and love nothing is possible. Our ambition to create a Christian Britain is the greatest we can take to ourselves. Because of its greatness, we know that it is beyond our power as human beings, and this knowledge should bring not discouragement but a greater hope. A Christian Britain implies not merely converts, but the conversion of social consciousness. It will appear in the lives of prophets—men who have not merely kept the faith through the dark age, but who have lived through the mind of that dark age, and got beyond it. The Christian prophets are not always recognized in their lives; or they may be stoned, or slain between the temple and the altar: but it is through them that God works to convert the habits of feeling and thinking, of desiring and willing, to which we are all more enslaved than we know.

I will end by saying something of one Christian witness of our own time, of whom you may never have heard. The name of Charles de Foucauld, a French priest who died in North Africa in 1916, is a name not well known in Britain, although his biography by René Bazin has been translated. I wish everyone would read that book, because I cannot, in a brief account of this extraordinary life, give you any conception of its spiritual quality. Foucauld was a man born to wealth and social position; he abandoned a life of pleasure and dissipation, first to travel in the disguise of a humble Jewish trader, with caravans in unexplored and unsubdued territory in French Morocco and Algeria. In constant danger of his life, he was able to make notes and surveys which proved of great value to the administration. Then he found a vocation for the religious life, lived for a time among the more austere communities, made a pilgrimage as a mendicant to the Holy Land, and finally, ordained a priest, became a missionary in a solitary African outpost. He qualified himself to give medical aid to the tribesmen. But the point is that he was something more than a good missionary, great as that vocation is. His aim was not primarily to convert by teaching, but to live the Christian life, alone among the natives. The people of Islamic countries recognize and venerate holiness whatever the religion of the saint; and the name of Père Foucauld was revered far and wide not only by his converts, but by fanatical Moslems. Almost

by an accident, he was killed at his prayers in 1916 by a maraud-
ing band to which his name and reputation were unknown.

This is not, as the world judges, a life of striking success. Yet if
you read his biography you will, I think, agree that through the
mysterious power of holiness, which is the power of God, he
achieved something for the world which should make us feel
very modest about all our schemes and plans. I think that it is
through such men as Foucauld that the reborn Christian consciousness comes; and I think that from the point of view which
we should take, there is no higher glory of a Christian empire
than that which was here brought into being by a death in the
desert.

Christian and Natural Virtues

Part of the *Christian News-Letter*, 3 September 1941

IT is often in my mind that we may tend to make the Christian compromise with the world—for some compromise must be made—on the wrong ground. We may go too far on the assumption that a little Christianity all round is more important than the full Christian life on the part of a few—as if the operation of the leaven on the lump could be performed once for all, after which we would have no need for leaven. It is not irrelevant or without significance, I think, that there are signs of a similar attitude with regard to culture and the arts: that a degree of refinement of manners and sensibility which cannot be attained by all, is taken to be superfluous and anti-social; and that works of art which cannot be enjoyed by all are to be condemned—even though there is evidence that popular art is continually fertilized and revivified from above. (I would instance poster art and the recent *Fantasia* of Mr Disney.) This form of egalitarianism would be destructive of either culture or Christianity. Full Christian virtue cannot exist without full Christian belief: but there is natural virtue about which Christian and non-Christian can agree.

That natural virtue should be presented as Christian virtue has unfortunate consequences in both directions. On the one hand the specifically Christian virtues get overlooked; and on the other hand, when standards of behaviour which should be accepted by all are put forward as Christian, they may appear to those who are not Christians to have no application to themselves. This country, like some others, has suffered grievously already by the decline of Christian belief and conduct: but, looking back at the twenty years between wars, one is inclined to assert that there were lapses, not only of Christianity, but of common social and personal virtues without which no society, Christian or not, can survive. There is, for instance, nothing particularly Christian about the capacity for responsible leadership in public life.

Amongst the natural virtues the place of which has not been settled I should include *patriotism*. I speak of it as being fundamentally a virtue, though obviously it can easily pass into the vices of nationalism, imperialism in the bad sense, collective pride and collective cupidity: it can, furthermore, be a cloak for individual or sectional selfishness. These associations are so patent that the word itself seems to have, for many people, attached to itself suspicion and odium—though the adjective 'unpatriotic' has never, so far as I know, acquired any but a strongly condemnatory meaning. There is another reason why we are shy of the word, in this country, and that is a question of good manners: we feel it to be a quality which is better taken for granted, and not talked about—though this particular reticence may be partly the outcome of more than a century of success and security. Yet it is a permanent feeling, which for better as well as worse cannot be exorcized: to ignore it, in our schemes for the federation of the world, as well as for our enemies to ignore it in their schemes of domination, is to risk eventual explosions. It includes the attachment to natural as well as to constructed surroundings, to place as well as to people, to the past as well as to the future; the attachment of a people to its own culture, and to its ability to make that specific and voluntary contribution to Christendom and to the world. Patriotism is a loyalty which requires to be balanced by other loyalties. One has, on the personal level, an attachment to people of one's own sort, among other nationalities: if one has them, to foreign friends; if one is a man of science or of art or of scholarship, to one's colleagues in foreign countries. There is the wider loyalty to justice. And finally, there is for the Christian the greatest and most binding of loyalties, which, like the loyalty to justice but with still greater authority, can bring him into conflict with the conception of patriotism prevailing at the moment. But higher loyalty does not supersede patriotism, but refines it: and the patriotism of a Christian should be something finer than that of a non-Christian, yet remain a common virtue shared with him. To speak of this subject at all, at a time when so much heroic self-sacrifice has manifested itself, may seem at first an impertinence; but I am not exhorting people to be more patriotic, but suggesting that we might think about the place of patriotism in the Christian life.

Freedom in Wartime

Part of the *Christian News-Letter*, 21 August 1940

ONE of the perennial problems of Christian thought is that of the different, and often conflicting, claims of liberty and order; sometimes between liberty and social justice. The difficulties of the problem are never more acute and perplexing than at a time like the present. When a nation is engaged in a vital struggle which revives the sense of community, social injustice is more patent and more intolerable, and demands control of the actions of some in the interests of all. At the same time our jealousy for our liberties, our fear of falling into the same servitude as that imposed by the régime against which we fight, becomes more sensitive. It is never easy to determine what are essential liberties, what are relative, and what are merely licence and indulgence: circumstances will alter our classifications. The fear of anarchy, or the fear of tyranny, may drive us to extremes in turn. A case in point is the outcry against the use of investigators (the so-called 'snoopers') by the Ministry of Information—a form of enquiry which, in any case, does not appear to have been introduced by the present Minister. Whether the methods are right, and the results useful, ought to be the subject of dispassionate examination. I have not seen either the methods or the purpose seriously criticized; but the Ministry has been the object of a clamour which would give the impression that it was endeavouring to set up a Secret Police.

The insistence of the problem of freedom led me to give close attention to Sir Norman Angell's recent Penguin pamphlet, *Why Freedom Matters*. To deal with the subject in 134 pages, Sir Norman wisely limits the terms of reference. He restricts himself to the 'fundamental and supreme freedom'—that is, 'the freedom to know, freedom of thought, of opinion, of discussion; free access to the raw materials of thought and discussion, to knowledge, particularly to knowledge of the facts relative to policies pursued by governments: freedom to know what our rulers are doing with our lives; freedom to discuss the facts in speech and print; the freedom described by Milton as "the liberty to know, to utter and to argue freely, according to conscience, which is above all liberties"'.

Such sentiments are unexceptionable; but they are not easy to apply. The universal accessibility of knowledge (by which the author appears to mean information) takes for granted a public, not necessarily of saints, but at least of Sir Norman Angells, who have highly trained minds. Knowledge requires a knower, as well as facts to be known: the question of the supply of knowers implies the whole problem of education. The problem of 'freedom of thought' is related to the problem of how to provide people who can think freely—and wisely. That is an educational problem: but the first problem of education is that of what rights should be conceded to and what duties imposed upon parents; and this is also the first problem of freedom.

This is not to say that I do not agree with the general tenor of Sir Norman Angell's argument in favour of free speech. But a Christian argument would have to take into account a great deal that Sir Norman does not treat; such as the problems of education and parental rights and responsibilities, just mentioned. And if it did not go so far as that, it would confine itself to particular liberties, and content itself with saying: here and here liberty is being infringed, let us defend it.

Let us consider a particular problem of freedom and order. In our Letter No. 41 the Editor commented upon the action of the City Council of York in terminating the engagement of all City employees who have declared themselves to be conscientious objectors. We should add that a strong letter of protest against this action appeared in the *Yorkshire Evening Press* of 2 August over the signatures of eleven Free Church ministers of that city. Such a statement is very welcome.

Nevertheless, there is one possible source of ill-feeling against conscientious objectors, which ought to be discussed freely, in order that it may not gain volume in subterranean channels. To several of our correspondents it appears unjust that able-bodied objectors of military age should remain in their peace-time employment, under the same conditions and enjoying the same income, while their contemporaries are being enlisted into new and often uncongenial services at meagre rates of pay and at risk of life. Such an inequality will no doubt be a greater grievance to the families of the men in the services than to the men themselves: the womenfolk may have bitter daily reminder of the difference in their situation and that of their children, from that of the families of the conscientious objectors. Such considerations may have influenced the members of the York City Council, and led them, in the attempt to remove one injustice, to commit another.

As for the financial inequality, it might be possible to remedy that by continuing the objectors in their posts at a reduced wage for the period of the war, making allowance for any higher scale of living, than that of a private soldier, which their several employments imposed: this again would only be fair if the difference in their salaries were not retained by their employers (whether private or public corporations), but allocated to some public cause. As for conscientious objectors over military age, I take it that their opinions, so far as they keep them to themselves, and cannot be found guilty of trying to excite disaffection, are their own business. As for those of military age, who have been exempted by a tribunal, and unless they are such persons and in such positions that they are likely to do harm, there is nothing whatever to be said for dismissing them. On a lower level than that of pure justice, it may be deprecated as doing harm to our national reputation for tolerance and generosity; on a lower level still, at a time of extreme national effort, it is nonsensical to eject men from jobs where they are useful, and cast them out for public assistance or starvation.

It is well also if we can see the problem of justice as between conscientious objectors and those who accept the obligation of military service, in a larger context of social justice. 'To each according to his need', *The Times* has recently reminded us, is an old motto; and the larger question (especially insistent in a time of national emergency) is how far inequalities of income should be allowed, except so far as they represent inequalities of need and inequalities of service to the cause of the nation and of humanity. There is at least one kind of injustice which should, I think, be agreed about by all members of the community whatever their other convictions, and that would be the injustice of anyone's being allowed to accumulate a fortune out of business arising directly from the war.

The tribunals have a very difficult task, and however precisely the law was defined, the important qualifications for those who sit upon them would still be sympathy and understanding, the ability to respect sincerity as well as the ability to unmask fraud. Laxity is to be deprecated, but the influence of public opinion should be exercised to restrain justices from harassing the inarticulate applicant, from preaching sermons, or from exhibiting temper. A judge at one tribunal said to an objector: 'The room will be the pleasanter for your leaving.' We have more sympathy for a worried judge in another city, who complained that the applicants 'go off into a series of mental processes'—a form of seizure perhaps unknown on that bench. When the applicant is a Christian, he and the bench should, and often do, receive the assistance and counsel of his clergyman or minister.

While the universal protest against the scandals connected with internment, and the government's immediate response to public opinion, are gratifying symptoms, we cannot allow the whole problem of internment and deportation to be considered as one which has been settled once for all. We must remember that harm has been done which will take time to right, and some grievous harm that can never be put right. It is not merely a question of releasing those whom the nation could use, but all those, useful or not, who are not the nation's enemies; and not merely a question of releasing them, but of releasing them for something better than starvation. An understanding of their position is not yet universal. A letter which we have from a

correspondent who had been interned and released is very temp-
erate and reasonable in tone, and does not complain of ill-
treatment, but suggests that some of the officers in the camp
laboured under elementary misconceptions, implying a still
deeper misunderstanding of the nature of this war. One of them
remarked: 'I did not know that so many Jews were Nazis!' And
others also seemed to think that the prisoners were all sup-
porters—or at least loyal to—the present German regime.

The Diversity of French Opinion

Part of the *Christian News-Letter*, 28 August 1940

THERE may be many people in this country who have formed the impression that Catholic France has shown itself to be reactionary, defeatist, and anti-British; who believe, in short, that Catholic France is adequately represented by Marshal Pétain. Such opinions should be controverted from the start. I cannot expect that any defence of Catholic and Christian France will be admitted by those who maintain that the English Church, and for the matter of that the Roman Church in Britain and all the other Churches, are dominated by reactionary laymen and still more reactionary clergy. But perhaps those who are aware of the variety of social views held by church people in Britain, will be disposed to credit the existence of some variety in France, a nation amongst whom much greater extremes of political opinion have been wont to flourish, and with a more violent animosity, than is usual here.

I have no private source of information about recent events in France, and public information is meagre. But the temper of the French people, and their divisions, cannot have changed completely in a few weeks' time; furthermore, the events of this summer have been prepared, as we can see in retrospect, by the events of the last twenty years and more. There has indeed always been an extreme right-wing Catholicism, but also a Catholicism of the people—the latter on the whole democratic and republican in sentiment, but not, of course, Communistic. For the Catholicism of the people, Miss Barbara Ward, in a well-informed article in the August number of the *Christian*

Democrat, makes a point of great importance: the fact that Catholic allegiance is strongest, not so much among the agricultural peasantry, the heirs of the French Revolution, who, especially in the South-West, tend to a free-thinking radicalism tinged with a cynical scepticism, but among the industrial workers. The latter, of course, are most thickly settled in the North-East: it is, therefore, the more Catholic part of France which is under the German heel. It is among these industrial groups—extending into Belgium—that such beneficent popular religious organizations as 'JOC' (the *Jocistes*, or Jeunesse Ouvrière Catholique) have taken root. The intellectual expression of Christianity allied with progressive social views has appeared in the pages of *Esprit* and several other Christian but not clerical periodicals: *Esprit*, at least, was still being published quite recently. Such reviews debated freely matters of Christian sociology, and deserved the attention of all Christian reformers in other countries.

As for the Catholicism of the Right, the term comprehends more variety of tendencies and backgrounds than Miss Ward, in the article cited above, succeeds in making us realize. She speaks of it as having found a vehicle of expression in the *Action Française* (a name which refers both to a political movement and to the daily newspaper by which it has been propagated). But the chief figure in this group was Charles Maurras: a middle-class, meridional, free-thinking man of letters. As a prose stylist Maurras is unquestionably a master, and deserved his election to the Académie Française; as a political thinker he has made, in his time, considerable contributions: but as a stylist he was the disciple of Voltaire, Renan and Anatole France; as a political thinker he was the disciple of the positivist Auguste Comte rather than of Catholics like Bonald and Joseph de Maistre. Maurras—who now, I hear, supports the Pétain regime—is a man of powerful but narrow mind, who used to hate Germany, dislike (unless my suspicions were wrong) England; and who, because of his southern Provençal origins, was strongly pro-Italian in the dubious cause of 'Latin Mediterranean culture'. Like most of his group, he was ill-informed on foreign affairs; and he did not know enough of England to understand either the good or bad of British policy. The one man in his group with some understanding of foreign affairs was Jacques Bainville, a writer of brilliant and lucid mind, whose early death is much to be regretted, but who was, like Maurras, a free-thinker and a product of the post-Revolution bourgeoisie.

The attitude of Maurras towards the Church was simple: he made no pretence of Christian belief, but supported the Church as a social institution making for stability. How many of the hereditary Catholics, of the old families, he was able to attract I do not know. At the time when I was personally acquainted with him and with his entourage, I think that his following was more from the middle and lower middle classes. He waged, it is true, an incessant journalistic battle against political corruption—somewhat indiscriminately and with excessive violence. The more pious of the royalist aristocracy may have hesitated to associate themselves with this outspoken agnostic who made no bones about his lack of faith. He, on the other hand, with honest naïvety, could see no reason why Catholics could not support him if he supported them; and when his movement was condemned, and his newspaper put on the Index, by Pius XI in 1927, I am sure that he was genuinely surprised. (The interdict has since been lifted, on the basis, I believe, of certain assurances given; but he has never attracted back to him such uncompromising Catholics as Jacques Maritain and Georges Bernanos.) In imposing his censure, the Pope was doing more than simply reaffirming the policy of reconciliation with the Republic entered upon by Leo XIII: he was condemning a heresy which asserted that only one form of government, the monarchical, was compatible with Catholicism. Perhaps also condemning a dangerous intolerance which classified Jews, Protestants and Freemasons in one comprehensive condemnation. I defended the *Action Française* when it was put upon the Index; my *particular* defence may or may not stand; but I believe now that the Pope understood its tendencies better. There was reason for dissatisfaction with the paper on secular grounds as well: not only its unsatisfactory treatment of foreign affairs, but its lack of appreciation of the importance of economics.

The *Action Française* is a middle-class movement of men of post-Revolution mentality. Until recent times, however, it held itself apart from explicitly Fascist movements such as the *Croix de Feu*. But my reason for writing of it at such length is that the 'extreme Right' is a term which includes at least three elements: the aristocratic families which have remained Catholic, and overlapping with them the military families; a certain number of middle-class ideologues, either non-Catholic or neo-Catholic; and finally quite a distinct lot, such financiers and large industrialists as calculate that their bread is buttered on that side. It certainly includes a number of ecclesiastics—but French ecclesiastics differ in their views just as do ordinary men and English ecclesiastics. There are no doubt many Catholics who are quite disinterested and honestly mistaken, who will have leisure to repent later of a sympathy for Italy which has only helped to put their country into the power of Germany: in a time of such political confusion there is every excuse for an honest mistake. But opinion is very diverse, and for this diversity we may call as evidence the great difference between Catholics about the war in Spain. A group of the Right (including several of the hierarchy) issued a manifesto in favour of Franco; the Communists, together with some Liberals, supported a declaration in favour of the Republic; but a group of the most eminent Catholics, including Maritain and François Mauriac (and including, if my memory is not at fault, several Protestants also) issued a statement of admirable fairness and Christian charity, which earned them the displeasure of both Right and Left. We must not forget, either, those great Catholic writers, such as Charles Péguy and Léon Bloy, who have united a fervent devotion to a passion for social justice; or the admirable work in theology and Christian philosophy which France has produced in the last twenty years, such as the devotional studies of Père Garrigou-Lagrange and the sociological work of Père Lallemant. The Church in France is better represented by these scholars, and by the *Jociste* workers under the German oppression, than by a few distinguished military men who, we must believe, have been honourably deluded.

I have left myself little space for drawing the comparison which suggests itself. We owe it to our Ally to try to understand her strength and weakness, and need this understanding if we are to contribute to the future shape of Europe. And we owe it to ourselves because it will help us to appraise our own situation. There is in this country no parallel as yet to the violence and extremity of the political divisions in France—divisions which have temporarily cancelled, but cannot extirpate, French patriotism. There is in this country a more solid basis for unity in patriotism; those who need reassurance on this point should read an article by Mr J. B. Priestley, whose broadcast talks have done so much to make articulate our faith in the actual, and our hope for the new Britain, in the August *World Review*. It is a unity in which the term 'Christian' does not excite faction; but though more unified, we cannot pride ourselves that we are more 'Christian' as a nation than are the French Christians as a part of a nation. It is a unity in which, I believe, there is more common willingness for sacrifice and for social change than we give ourselves credit for. But the unity which has affirmed itself in war may easily disintegrate in peace; and for peace it will need the element of a more conscious, united and intrepid body of Christian thought and practice than it can yet boast.

The Christian Education
of France

Part of the *Christian News-Letter*, 3 September 1941

WE know little of the situation in either occupied or unoccupied France; and those of us who have French friends receive no news, or hardly more than that they are still alive. Our public preoccupation, also, is with the foreign policy of the Vichy government and its immediate consequences for us. Yet it is of very great importance, in the long run, that we should take every opportunity of informing ourselves about the domestic policy of that government, and of the changes taking place inside France. For the problem of France will be one of the most vital and difficult of all the post-war problems; and we need to remind ourselves that the France which we shall have to get to know—after a period of isolation of the two countries from each other for which there is no parallel in history—may be different from the France which we knew up to fifteen months ago. For that reconstruction of understanding which will be essential, we shall need all our powers of imagination, sympathy and tolerance; and also all the information about the steps in France's development that we can meanwhile obtain. The article in *The Times* of 14 August, therefore, meagre as it is, deserves our careful attention.

As for the abolition of political parties, we know well that there were formerly far too many for parliamentary government to be anything but a tedious farce; and we know how prevalent was political corruption and venality. As for the abolition of Free Masonry, we must remember that the Grand Orient was a very different affair from Free Masonry as known in Britain—I have always understood that relations between the two bodies were broken off long ago. On the other hand, the abolition of secret societies seems to have come rather late, for it arouses our recollection of the fact that some of the most dangerous of these, in the years before the war, were freely said to have been abetted and subsidized by Germany, if not even created by German machinations. What gives us the gravest anxiety, is the statement (in the *Times* article cited) that 'Jews have been given a special status, based on the laws of Nuremberg, which makes their condition little better than that of bondsmen.' Anti-Semitism there has always been, among the parties of the extreme Right: but it was a very different thing, as a symptom of the disorder of French society and politics for the last hundred and fifty years, from what it is when it takes its place as a principle of reconstruction. If this is what is happening, we can only hope that there has been, or that there will be, some organized protest against such injustice, by the French ecclesiastical hierarchy: unless we are also optimistic enough to hope that these measures are only taken under the strongest pressure from Germany, and that no French government, once that government was master in its own house, would enforce such measures or keep them on its statutes. But unless the French Church, and the Protestant bodies in France rise to protest, we must feel serious doubts about the way in which the revival of Christian France, advertised from Vichy, is to be carried out.

In Spain—a country which I do not know—it may be that the vast majority of the population, however anti-clerical, is Christian and Catholic at heart. France has had a very different story. We may deplore the French Revolution, but we must accept it as a fact. In no European country is the gulf between the Christian and the non-Christian more acute; a large part of the population is the product of four generations of apostasy, and is therefore not to be Christianized overnight or made to conform to behaviour the principles of which it denies. What four generations have destroyed cannot in one generation be recreated; and the unity which France so sorely needs will not be achieved by oppression.

The words which I have used will, I hope, come with more

force from one who has never been an admirer of Republican government in France. The device *Liberté, Egalité, Fraternité* is only the memorial of the time of revolution: *Famille, Travail, Patrie* has more permanent value. But to substitute the second for the first is to go further than merely to call attention to equal, or even to higher values: it is by implication the denial and repudiation of the first. It suggests the danger of a reaction which might be as bad, or worse than that from which it reacts. To have affirmed Liberty, Equality, Fraternity in that way was, I think, unfortunate: but to repudiate them in this way is at least an equal error. Every country needs a strong government; it is probable that France in her present condition can only be ruled by an autocratic government; but at no time can an autocratic government be good for France unless it has the wisdom and prescience to recognize limits to autocracy. No one who knows and loves France can wish to see her revert to the condition of the twenty years between the wars: but reactionary excesses might foment a counter-reaction to a condition equally deplorable.

I am not suggesting that we have enough information yet to judge the domestic and cultural policy of the present government of unoccupied France: we have merely enough to be apprehensive, and to make it imperative for us to follow the progress of this policy as well as conditions of communication permit. It is especially important that the Christian public here should concern itself with the methods of a government which professes Christianity, and which proclaims the ideal of a Christian France. For we have the same ideal for Britain, and can surely profit by studying the success or failure of other methods than our own.

Education in a Christian Society

The Supplement to the *Christian News-Letter*, 13 March
1940

MY only justification for attempting to write about education in a Christian society is that no one else has so far done so. The problems of education in a secular society—but perhaps the right word is neither *secular* nor *pagan*, but *infidel*—have been dealt with again and again by those who can speak from vocation, knowledge and experience; and some of the writers who speak with authority on these problems are men of strong Christian convictions. And the subject of religious instruction in schools, under contemporary conditions, is receiving a good deal of attention. My subject is education in a society which should be Christian in the sense and to the degree indicated in my book *The Idea of a Christian Society*. I was not there concerned with the means to be employed to bring such a society into existence; and I am not here concerned with the means of realizing a Christian education. Yet I maintain that it is well to have some notion of where we want to go before we arrange to start upon a journey; and, accordingly, while I am concerned with the end and not the means, I believe that our conception of the end should not be wholly without influence upon our action.

The lack of any clear notion of the end seems to me to impair much contemporary discussion of education. One error into which we may fall is that of assuming that our social framework is always going to be what it has been and elaborating our reforms within that frame: this might be described as an attempt to give our fathers and grandfathers a better education—and our fathers and grandfathers are no longer in need of any re-education that we could give them. The other mistake, and one to which in these times we are more prone, is to plan for a 'changing world'—but on the assumption, that we all too readily make, that we have a pretty shrewd idea of what the changes are going to be. This form of gambling has the disadvantage that however the world changes—and I concede that our world is likely to change with great rapidity—a great deal of the change will be unexpected, and some of it unrecognized when it comes. It is like cutting clothes for a child which is growing fast, but not at a steady rate and in regular proportions: the child will always be finding itself in a new suit which doesn't fit, and which never will fit. All that we can say for such reforms is that, if they do not give us a better education, they will at least give us one which is not wrong in the same respects. Prudence advises us to restrict our reforms to patching and changing here and there, not committing ourselves to a desperate hazard on what the future is going to be like. But at the same time reason counsels us to avoid surrendering ourselves either to a present which is already past or to a future which is unknown, and to look below the surface of apparent fixity or inscrutable change in search of those educational values which can be regarded as permanent. We hear a good deal of 'social philosophy' and of the 'philosophy of education', as well as of the 'sociological attitude': but if the philosophy is to be more than a philosophy of flux, it must endeavour to determine what are these permanent values.

I suggest that the values which we most ignore, the recognition of which we most seldom find in writings on education, are those of Wisdom and Holiness, the values of the sage and of the saint. I have no need, in the *Christian News-Letter*, to attempt to define these terms; but it is as well to remind ourselves, that there are innumerable people today to whom the terms would be meaningless even if I defined them. In the East, and in pre-Christian Europe, the sage and the saint have been hardly distinguishable from each other. We must recognize the truth in both the Oriental and the Christian views. In the East, it must be remembered, the sage as the educated man at the highest stage—the *sadhu*, or *mahatma*, or whatever other word you use—was a person who had educated his emotions and sensibility, as well as his mind, by the most arduous application to study. The Christian West, on the other hand, while ready to recognize and to canonize the union of intellectual and spiritual excellence in one person (St Thomas Aquinas and St John of the Cross are two types of such union) has held a doctrine of divine grace unknown to the Orient, and has always recognized saintliness in the humble and unlearned as well. I believe, of course, that Christianity is right; but Christianity in its decayed forms could learn much from the East. For our tendency has been to identify wisdom with knowledge, saintliness with natural goodness, to minimize not only the operation of grace but self-training, to divorce holiness from education. Education has come to mean education of the mind only; and an education which is only of the mind—of the mind in its restricted modern sense—can lead to scholarship, to efficiency, to worldly achievement and to power, but not to wisdom.

What is known as 'education for culture' and what is known as 'character-building' are the atrophied vestiges of wisdom and holiness. In a Christian society we should not educate primarily either for culture or for character; but culture and character might be by-products of our education, as technical efficiency would be incidental to it.

In this context I may refer to the classification of Max Weber, which, as I only know it at second hand, I should be diffident in mentioning, but that it may be known to readers of this paper from Professor Clarke's *Education and Social Change*. Weber distinguishes three main types of education throughout history: *charismatic education, education for culture, specialist education*. I shall not criticize such a classification without having read the defence of it, which no doubt the inventor gives. As an account of historical process from primitive times to the present day, it may be very satisfactory within the author's frame of reference. The term *charismatic education* does not sound very happy, inasmuch as 'charismatic' means 'pertaining to a favour or grace from God'; and the relation between grace and education is not clear. But it probably meant more to Professor Weber than it does to Professor Clarke: to whom, in the book I have just mentioned, it seems to mean hardly more than the practice by which Sir John Falstaff lost his voice—'halloing and singing of anthems'. Professor Mannheim defines charismatic education clearly by saying that it

> is dominant in the magical period or in periods in which religion reaches its highest point. In the first case it wants to arouse hidden powers latent in man, in the second to awaken religious intuition and the inner readiness for transcendental experience. In both cases the predominant aim is not the transfer of a certain concrete content or skill but that of stirring up certain innate powers which are, if not superhuman, at least the limited possession of the chosen.

I can hardly suppose that this is meant to comprehend the whole of the education of the 'primitive races' any more than of the higher races in their religious phase; because in the highly organized societies of Polynesia, surely, you can find all three types of education, charismatic, cultural and specialized, very well coordinated. And in the higher religious education of India a great deal of what Mannheim, in the passage quoted above, calls 'transfer of concrete contents' takes place: the study of the sacred Scriptures. Nevertheless, the category of charismatic education seems to approximate most nearly of the three to what I mean by the central values of Christian education—with this reservation, that it looks very different from the inside.

At this point, I make no doubt, many readers will have come to the conclusion that I am quite prepared to dispense altogether, in the Christian Society, with everything that they know and value by the name of education—to the conclusion, in fact, that my goal is in effect a relapse into barbarism. I will say, therefore, in the hope that it may help, that I am not anxious to scrap anything, and that I recognize the need for laboratories and technical schools, as well as for institutions for the study of history and philosophy and ancient and modern languages, in any future society that I can desire or imagine. I am not envisaging, either, a society of saints or adepts. The important question is: What is the type of man which a society holds in highest honour? What is the type of man—below the heights of the greatest genius or of the greatest infusion of grace—which it is proudest to produce? Whatever ideals a society maintains (and it is not necessarily conscious of what its real ideals are) will insensibly influence its whole system of education, will affect the way in which it teaches, the way in which it acquires, the way in which it uses, the most apparently remote or specialized disciplines.

There is certainly no system to which we can go back. The ideals of *The Governour*, the ideals of John Locke, those of Thomas Arnold, are all equally exhausted and inapplicable to any future Christian society. And while wisdom and holiness are, of course, unchanging, yet the technique of attaining them will change, and the technique of inculcating a right attitude towards them on the part of the vast majority of human beings who can attain as a minimum (and it is no small thing to attain) the right attitude towards them—the right attitude which is the starting point from which salvation may be come by.

The scope of education is no longer the task of merely training individuals in and for a society, but also the much larger task of training a society itself—without our having any fundamental accepted principles on which to train it. The scope of education has been rapidly expanding as social organisms have broken down and been replaced by the mechanization which increases, while it manipulates, the atomization of individuals.

There results a good deal of confusion of motives about the immediate reforms that are advocated. A case in point is that of the school-leaving age. I do not hold any fixed opinion as to what this age should be. I am quite prepared to be persuaded that under the conditions in which the greater part of our population lives, there is everything to be said for raising the age to eighteen. I only suggest that we ought to consider whether it should not be our purpose to change these conditions, rather than merely adapt our system of education to them. It is better that boys and girls should be at school than that they should be subject to industrial exploitation, in an environment where family influence is negligible or even harmful, and where local community does not

exist. But a change which is all to the good in certain circumstances is not necessarily a change for the better *absolutely*; and it
makes all the difference whether we acknowledge that such a
change is merely making the best of a bad job, or whether we
pretend that it is good in itself. Is this further education necessarily going to make the majority wiser or better people?

I am excepting the number of those who possess the ability to
acquire special techniques—as of the various kinds of engineer-
ing; assuming that their being trained to exercise this ability will
be of advantage to society. But it is at least an open question,
whether for the majority of human beings there is not an
optimum amount of school instruction, and an optimum
amount of knowledge, that they are able to acquire without
excessive and deleterious strain. It is at least an open question,
whether we cannot injure society and the individual as much by
over-education, as by not providing enough.

I do not wish to prejudice the answers to such questions; I only
say that they ought to be raised, and that they can only be rightly
answered if we keep hold of the right ultimate values of education, and if we see the problems of education in right relation to
the problems of society, and hold the right values there also.

I cannot help suspecting, however, that it is possible that
education, in the meaning of the word which it has in contemporary society, is over-valued—by being contrasted simply
with the *absence of itself*, and not with anything positive. With this
thought in mind, I think that the claims of 'equalization of
opportunity', and the 'democratization of education' ought to be
scrutinized very carefully. I trust that no one will suppose me to
be a defender of a social order and an educational system based
upon income—the best thing to be said for which is that it
manages to keep up some *pretence* of being based upon breeding.
I am only apprehensive lest, as is so common in human affairs,
we see the defects and dangers of the system we would institute
less clearly than those of that which we would replace. The
concept of 'opportunity' can be a very dangerous one if we are
not severe in our standards of what it is desirable to have opportunity *for*. Unless society can exercise some unconscious

pressure upon its members to want the right things, the right life, the opportunity given may be merely the opportunity to follow false lights, the opportunity to follow aims for which the individual is unsuited, or which are not to the advantage of society. There will (I hope) always be a few individuals who will follow their own aims, independent of the social influences by which they are surrounded, unfettered by fear or flattery: it is probably to the advantage of society, even, that it should nourish a few anti-social people. But for the great majority, 'opportunity' may be no more than opportunity to aim to excel (or at least keep their end up) at whatever the people with whom they associate think admirable. I am not the enemy of opportunity; I only say that in providing opportunity you are assuming a very grave responsibility. Unless, at least, you hold a doctrine of the natural goodness of man (and even so you can hardly avoid admitting the corruption of society) you have the responsibility of inculcating the right values.

Equalization of opportunity, then, and democratization of education, are in danger of becoming uncriticized dogmas. They can come to imply, as an ultimate, a complete mobility of society—and of an *atomized* society. I mean by this that many of those who hold these two principles may be unconsciously carrying them over from nineteenth-century liberalism—and in so far as they spring from liberalism they may end in totalitarianism. It is to think of the individual in isolation, apart from family and from local milieux, as having certain intellectual and sensitive capacities to be nurtured and developed to their full extent; and of a system of education as a vast calculating machine which would automatically sort out each generation afresh according to a culture-index of each child. The result might be to produce a race of spiritual nomads. Again, I wish only to raise issues, not to prejudice them. But it seems to me that there is a danger in simplifying the concept of society into the individual and the nation, and ignoring all the organic groupings in between; and it seems to me possible that in a healthy society there must be an element of fixity *and* an element of mobility, and that the problem lies in this adjustment.

These considerations may seem to have taken me far afield from the main point of this letter—the affirmation of the end values of Christian education as wisdom and holiness. I hope that anyone who makes this comment at this point may be persuaded to read again what I have said, and give me the benefit of another hearing; for I feel confident that it is only in the light of these two values that what I have just been saying can be appreciated.

The Christian Conception
of Education

A paper delivered to the Archbishop of York's
Conference at Malvern in 1941 and published in its
Proceedings (1942)

THERE are several problems which are distinct but intimately
related: which, therefore, should neither be confused nor considered without reference to each other. There is first the problem
of what should be done about Religious Education in the educational system as we have it at present. There is the problem of its
place in a system reformed according to the sort of pattern that is
likely or possible in the immediate future. There is also the
question of whether we need a specifically Christian doctrine of
education in general. It is with the third that this paper is concerned. This paper is not concerned with ideals and methods of
teaching Divinity, or with such reforms in education as we may
advocate as humane and enlightened people. It is not concerned
with Point 2 of the statement by the Archbishops, the
Cardinal-Archbishop and the Moderator, which reads as
follows:

> Every child, regardless of race or class, should have equal
> opportunities of education, suitable for the development of his
> peculiar capabilities.

Within the scope of my paper, this point is not an educational
point at all. The question whether every child should have equal
opportunities of education, and if so how the opportunities are
to be equalized, is primarily a question of social justice. The
question of education is primarily the question of what educa-

tion is and what sort of knowledge is in itself desirable. This question is sometimes ignored by those who see the problem of education only in terms of adapting our system to a changed and changing world, if they do not stop to enquire whether there are any permanent principles of education to which a changed and changing world should itself be brought to conform. What I am concerned with here, as I have said, is the need for a specifically Christian doctrine of education. I make no attempt to indicate what that doctrine should be; I am only urging the case for recognizing the need for it.

My question 'whether the leadership of the Church requires a conception of education' is secondary to another, which can be put as follows: 'is an adequate and purposeful conception of education possible without the leadership of the Church?' If our answer to this second question is in the affirmative, the leadership of the Church is superfluous, and our answer to the first question must be in the negative: for if education can get on without the Church, the Church had better make up its mind not to meddle where it is not needed, and to confine itself to the struggle, in which it is already interesting itself, for an adequate and universal religious instruction in schools. If, on the other hand, we conclude that no adequate conception of education is possible without the leadership of the Church, then our policy about religious instruction will be considerably altered and extended; for it must become a policy not only of fitting religious instruction into whatever system of education happens to prevail, but a programme of what ought to be the system of education into which that religious instruction has to be fitted.

We must recognize at this point that the system according to which only religious instruction comes within the province of the Church, while the remainder of the educational field is a neutral territory in which the theologian and Christian philosopher has, as such, no interest, itself implies a theory of education—a theory so generally accepted that it remains implicit, and therefore all the more difficult to disturb. It is important to consider how this state of affairs came about. I can only offer a few hints of what has happened, leaving their amplification and correction to those who are better qualified.

During the nineteenth century two tendencies in education are observable. The first is the tendency, already noted by the prescient mind of Coleridge, for education to develop as instruction in an increasing number and variety of subjects which came to be assigned equal value, and from which no significant pattern was formed. This movement was fostered by several social and economic developments, as well as by the proliferation and specialized extension of natural sciences—each requiring for its practice a very high degree of training, and each (rightly enough) acquiring a dignity of its own. With the rapid multiplication of subjects of study and research, the relative values of which could hardly, at that stage of novelty and change, be assessed, the task of organization would have been herculean, and was hardly attempted: so that instead of getting what the situation called for, a number of educational patterns coordinated by dominant principles, we remain at the pioneer stage of accepting a number of unrelated courses for various careers. In America, where development and change in education naturally met with less resistance or criticism, this centrifugal tendency was even elevated into a principle; and it was maintained, by a distinguished educator of the last century (himself trained as a scientist) that one subject of instruction was as good as another for turning out an educated man. This belief the educator in question complemented by another (arising from that optimistic faith in the natural goodness of the human will which prevailed at the time and which perhaps a sounder theology might have corrected) to the effect that a youth of eighteen, entering a university, was competent to decide for himself what subject or combination of subjects could best provide him with a liberal education. The only criterion of whether a subject was necessary for your education, was whether you happened at the time to be interested in it.

This tendency, arising from the inability to cope with the rapid development of special sciences, was reinforced by another

with quite different causes. The beginning of overt secularization lies in non-sectarianism: that is, in the growth of a feeling of
injustice in the fact that differences of inherited religious
allegiance, springing from difference of opinion on certain
theological doctrines or certain forms of ecclesiastical organization, should exclude a man from an institution the advantages of
which he was otherwise well qualified to benefit by. In consequence, not only differences of doctrine, but adherence to *any*
religious faith, came to appear of little account.

I am concerned at the moment with what has happened in
America: but I believe that what has happened in America has
been happening here also; except for the special case of the public
schools, which has other symptoms on which I shall have to
comment presently. But the tendency in education which I have
been discussing has gone farther in America, and therefore it is
significant that a certain reaction against it, which calls itself
humanism, has originated in America. Humanism is significant
for our purpose because it represents an admission, from a
purely non-Christian point of view, that the results of what has
been happening are not altogether good. Humanism is, of
course, an attempt to devise a philosophy of life without a
metaphysic; and its champions have had much to say on other
subjects than education. But these champions—and of course I
mean Irving Babbitt and his disciples—have been mostly university professors; it was in the field of education that they first
observed the disintegrating influence of contemporary values
and ideals; and it was in this field that they spoke with most
authority and to the best purpose. Again the ideals of specialized
or miscellaneous instruction, of technical narrowness or of dilet-
tante smattering, they opposed the ideals of unity and wisdom. It
is true that the attention of the humanists was concentrated on
the particular area of their own experience and activity, that of
education at the college and university stage: but the principles
which they defended had their implications for primary and
secondary education as well. Their battle is by no means won.
There are only sporadic evidences of a movement in that direction, in attempts to give a greater coordination to undergraduate

work in some of the older universities—designing the changes partly on the models of the Oxford and Cambridge methods in humane studies—and some interesting experiment at the University of Chicago and at smaller institutions such as St John's, Annapolis. Some of these attempts have been limited by the defective foundations of school education. For my present purpose, however, the immediate influence of humanistic ideas of education is not to the point. The question is, are the humanist ideals enough—enough, not only from our point of view, but to perform what the humanists hope of them?

On the answer to this question a good deal depends. For if a secular or non-religious humanism can provide an adequate foundation for general education, such that from our point of view it requires only to be supplemented by religious instruction, then we not only have a common ground with the wiser, though smaller body of non-Christian educational theorists, but we could afford to leave to the disciples of Irving Babbitt in America and such groups as Dr Leavis and his friends in this country, the elaboration and implementing of policies. We should then be forced to say, in response to the question to which I am speaking, that the leadership of the Church could *not* depend upon 'an adequate and purposeful conception of education'. For unless the Church can provide a truer philosophy of education than any non-Christian philosophy can produce, its vital concern with education is not obvious. I hold, however, that humanism of its nature stops short of a philosophy; that education must rest upon a dogmatic view whether natural or supernatural; and that in education as in other matters, the only final alternative to a worldly totalitarian view is a Christian view. We may be in accord with the humanists, in everything they want; they may be invaluable allies; but we must remember that Christian doctrine provides the only rational justification for the programme which we may share with them.

Humanism is, in fact, derived from Christianity and contingent upon it; unexplainable and unacceptable except as the outcome of Christian tradition. (I have argued this point elsewhere, and I do not propose to go further into the matter here.) I know that its adherents have derived great comfort from Buddhism and from Confucianism: but the habits of thinking and feeling upon which they rely are habits resulting from centuries of Christian tradition.[1] You can be eclectic in ideas, but you have no such freedom to choose your ancestors. In urging that education should aim at forming, not merely the instructed man or the technically competent man but the *wise* man, they restore a much needed emphasis; and no one should assert that wisdom is to be acquired only from the study of Christian authors. But wisdom is one thing without Christian wisdom, and another thing with it; and there is a sense in which wisdom that is not Christian turns to folly. Furthermore, wisdom is no substitute for faith; and however strongly convinced, cannot give a ground for its conviction. It is the product of experience of men and of books, of arts and of actions, and it can only appeal to the experiential test. To those who ridicule its advice, it can only say 'try your way and see'; and afterwards it has the cold consolation of saying 'I told you so.' Its work is of the nature of a commentary, and the wisdom of Europe since the Christian revelation has been dependent upon the Christian tradition: what would be the significance of Montaigne or of La Rochefoucauld without the Christian background? Such considerations as these go to explain why humanism as a way of life, and in particular as a way of education, is not enough. It can only appeal to a small number of superior individuals; it can help them to recognize what is wrong, but it cannot provide them with the power to influence the mass of mankind and to bring about what is right. It can appeal to those people who have already the humanists' feelings and desires: but it cannot change the will of those who worship false gods. It is powerless against the drifting desires or torrential passions which turn by turn provide the motive force for the

---

[1] I would not, however, minimize the importance of their contribution in reminding us of the need for a Christian examination and understanding of Eastern thought, which the Christian philosophy of the future cannot afford to neglect. With the professed humanists, in this work, I should associate the name of Dr I. A. Richards.

mass of natural men. Humanistic wisdom can provide a helpful, if in the end joyless nourishment for the intelligent educated individual—on another level, there is a comparable wisdom of the countryman rooted in village tradition and the life of the countryside and the procession of the seasons—but it cannot sustain an entire society. In the field of education, the humanistic approach may lead to many valuable reforms; but it seems to me inherent in the humanistic position to make unexamined assumptions, which it is likely to be right in making, but which it cannot justify.

I have read an admirable article by Dr Leavis, which appeared some months ago in *Scrutiny*, in which he makes very sensible suggestions for the improvement of the English Tripos. In this article he observes: 'the problem of producing the "educated man"—the man of humane culture who is equipped to be intelligent and responsible about the problems of contemporary civilization—becomes that of realizing the Idea of a University in practical dispositions appropriate to the modern world.' And he quotes a sentence by a Mr Brooks Otis, an American writer: 'it is an urgently necessary work ... to explore the means of bringing the various kinds of specialist knowledge and training into effective relation with informed general intelligence, humane culture, social conscience and political will.' One agrees. But to such questions as: 'Why should we want humane culture? Why is one conception of humane culture better than another? What is the sanction for your conception of social conscience or of political will as against that, for instance, now dominant in Germany?' I do not think that the humanist can give a satisfactory answer.

Not every system of theology can lead us to an answer either. If one took a strictly Lutheran point of view, I suppose that the Church's interest in education would be only to produce the maximum number of believers practising worship and the Christian virtues; and the secular part of education would not be our business as Christians. But if we accept the five points put forward by the Archbishops, the Cardinal-Archbishop and the Moderator, we cannot take refuge in this limitation.

Point 2. Every child, regardless of race and class, should have equal opportunities of education, suitable for the development of his peculiar capacities.

If we accept this point, we are obliged, as Christians, to concern ourselves about what the child receives under the name of 'education'. The Christian interest cannot ask less than that every Christian child should be trained to *understand* his faith to the extent of his capacities—an expectation which is very far from being realized today—and this understanding of his faith requires the provision of some education in history, and for the more intelligent beyond early youth some education in philosophy as well. It requires also the study of literature, for you cannot draw any strict line between theological and non-theological writing, and you cannot have an ample understanding of Christian literature without seeing it in its setting of non-Christian literature. Every educated Christian should have some acquaintance with St Augustine and with Pascal—to mention only two great Christian names in literature; and you cannot understand St Augustine or Pascal without some study of the worlds in which they lived, and the literature, whether secular or pagan, on which their minds had been fed. Our education as Christians may require even the study of natural science. And this is not simply saying that you cannot have a full Christian education without supplementing it by a general education. The interpretation of these studies will be given a different pattern by educated Christian belief. The difference of pattern is most obvious in the case of the study of history: which must look very different to the Christian, to the student who interprets history according to some individual or group rationalization, as of Hegel or Marx, and to the scholar for whom it is merely a series of events with innumerable and unrelated causes. Furthermore, without abating our insistence upon the universality of the Church and the transcendence of Christian communion over national and racial differences, we must remember that education has to be fashioned according to the needs of particular peoples living in particular places: that the Church must be interested not only in those principles of education which are valid for all peoples at all times and in all places, but in their application to people of different countries with different traditions and different habits of mind, and in their several types and orders.

What I have just been saying took its departure from the consideration of the limits of humanistic ideals of education. But it will be said that neither the explicitly non-Christian humanism, nor the instructional system which humanism set out to battle against, is indigenous or deeply rooted in this country, and that I have overlooked the ideals of public school education since the time of Dr Arnold: that of 'education for character', and that of 'the Christian gentleman'. I do not propose to enquire whether it is not desirable that even those whom we do not educate to be 'gentlemen' should be educated to be Christians; or to enquire whether it is desirable to have two systems of education quite so sharply separated in their aims as we appear to have at present. I confine myself to the question whether the 'Christian education' associated with the name of Arnold has worn well enough to require no criticism. Those whose Christianity remains of the same kind as that professed by Dr Arnold will find only incidental defects. But the Christian doctrine of Arnold was one which would be vague, unsound and perhaps heretical at any time; and its practical weakness is more apparent today than it was two generations ago. It assumed that the nation was Christian, and that it would remain so; and it took for granted a Christianity *moyenne* which discouraged both complete lapse from profession and the more intense developments of religious feelings. And the idea of a 'national Christianity' provided no safeguard against this Christianity falling to a very low level. The Christian virtues were so closely united to the civic virtues as to be confounded with them. The distinction between Christian virtues and natural virtues becomes obliterated; honour becomes more important than morality; and indeed, for many men, the observances of a code of honour and good form in immorality is all that is left of Christian morals. Furthermore, the union of Church and State is one thing, their identification is another. The tendency has been, I think, towards a secularization of education apparently very different from that obvious in America, in the State-aided schools, in the provincial universities and increasingly in the older universities, but all the more insidious. In assuming the existence of a national Christian society and its continuance, the Christian education of Arnold provided no protection against the gradual diminution of Christian belief, and provided no weapons against the positive and militant anti-Christian movements of our time. And if education is not definitely orientated towards spiritual ends higher than those which Arnold set, it will, with the change in the temper of society, come to be orientated towards material ends, and of these a universal State system of education with the propagation of a universal State system of values—whether or not these masquerade as Christian—may be the inevitable consummation.

We cannot go back to the world as it appeared to be in the time of Dr Arnold. We shall not fundamentally mend matters simply by universalizing the 'public school system' (which might become something quite different, but not necessarily more Christian, in the process) and endeavouring to turn out a whole nation of 'Christian gentlemen'. Nor shall we effect the desired transformation merely by improving the standards and methods of religious instruction in schools, important as that task is. What is needed is a Christian doctrine of education which shall be part of a Christian doctrine of man. This demands hard thinking, for it is first of all theological thinking that must be done; and thinking about the general principles of Christian education must be followed by thinking which will be Christian sociology—for it must, to be applied, take into consideration the actual state of affairs in England, both material and spiritual, and the current tendencies of thought, feeling and behaviour. If we omit the first stage, as we are likely to do, we shall find ourselves merely planning to adapt our system of education to a 'changing world', without pausing to ask whether there are not permanent principles of what should be the goal of education, and permanent standards of quality, in relation to which we ought to try to direct the ways in which this changing world shall change.

I am not here occupied with 'the idea of a Christian society', and even if I were, my programme would not include the handing over of educational control to the Church. A State Church, or any Church, as a bureaucratic authority directing the education of the country, might turn out no better, perhaps worse, or perhaps not very different from the State itself; and we ought to aim to avoid, not promote, centralization and standardization. The task of the Church is to christianize the State and society, not to take over any of the functions either of the State or of private groups or foundations. And if it is to christianize education—which involves, as I have tried to say, not merely an insistence upon religious instruction, but the revolutionizing of educational ideals—some of its members must be prepared to give time to long and hard thought. The task in view is not to be accomplished by appointing commissions to do our thinking for us, or to arrive at conclusions and make recommendations before the thinking has been half done. It is not to be accomplished by conferences and manifestos, but by the patient toil of various minds in the humble and submissive hope of the direction of the Holy Ghost. The first step is perhaps the most difficult of all, for it is simply to change our minds—to see the relationships and responsibility of the Church towards education as we have not seen it before; to see that religious instruction is only a part of this relationship and responsibility; and to see that unless the soul of education is inspired by Christianity it will fall a prey to such worldliness as will make the more limited efforts of religious teaching to be in vain.

On the Place and Function
of the Clerisy

A Paper written by T. S. Eliot for discussion at
the Moot Meeting of December 1944

THE subject presents itself to me first in the form of three questions:

> What is the place of the clerisy, if it exists, in the social structure?
> Assuming it to exist, what is its composition?
> In view of its composition, what is its function?

The clerisy (if it exists) must be an *élite* and not a *class*. The distinction may appear too obvious to need mention, yet I suspect that in discussion the two are often confused. An élite is not a substitute for a class, or a class for an élite. This might be put simply by saying that the unit of the class is the family, and the unit of the élite the individual. A man is born a member of a class, but becomes a member of an élite by virtue of individual superiority developed by training; he does not thereby cease to be a member of the class into which he was born, nevertheless he is partially separated from the other members of his class who are not members of the same élite. No man can change his class, but his successful effort or his incapacity may, and often does, result in his children belonging to a somewhat different class from his own.

We have therefore to consider élites against the background of class. The position of an élite in a class society would no doubt be very different; but we have no experience, and no historical knowledge, of such a society, except perhaps at a very low stage of development. It is sometimes assumed, by those who want to eat their cake and have it too, that the advantages of a class society, without its disadvantages, can be obtained by having a classless society with a systematic selection of individuals who will form an élite. But to destroy the foundations of the class (the transmission of advantages from one generation to the next) is to destroy what has produced the good element in class as well as the bad. You will get something quite different; and you do not know what it will be like. (This, I think, is the fundamental criticism of Happold's *Towards a New Aristocracy*.[1]) I am not here concerned with whether such a social structure would be better or worse; I only think that it is better to begin by considering what the clerisy is and has been in such society as we know, before considering what it ought to be in a different form of society.

One of the chief merits of class is that it is an influence for stability; one of the chief merits of the clerical élite is that it is an influence for change. To some extent, therefore, there is, and I think should be, a conflict between class and clerical élite. On the one hand, the clerical élite is dependent upon whatever is the dominant class of its time;[2] on the other hand, it is apt to be critical of, and subversive of, the class in power. (This peculiar dual relationship may be illustrated from the position and influence of the French *philosophes* under the *ancien régime*, and that of such men as Carlyle, Ruskin and Arnold in the upper-middle-class Victorian era.)

When we speak of class, we must sometimes be thinking of a division of two, or three classes; and sometimes of the innumerable and almost imperceptible subdivisions which are characteristic of English society. Unless we keep both in mind at once we are liable to fall into error. Hence, when we say that the

[1] Published by Faber in autumn 1943. (None of these footnotes is by Eliot.)
[2] Cf. the more recent observation of a sociologist, W. L. Guttsman: 'The contemporary [political] élite cannot easily be seen in isolation and apart from the character and power of a wider upper class from which so many of its members are recruited. ... The membership of élite groups is largely recruited from men who belong in any case to the upper layers of society.' *The British Political Elite* (London: MacGibbon, 1963), pp. 320–1.

majority of the clerisy have in the past been drawn from the middle class, we mean that above and below two not very distinct frontiers, very few distinguished 'clerics' are to be found. They come from the middle, though when compared one with another great differences of background appear. But the origins of the clerisy are one thing, and their relation to the dominant class another. The history of English literature can be traced in relation to the publics for which the men of letters wrote (not precisely the public which read their works or saw their plays, but the public which, consciously or unconsciously, they aimed to please or interest). The general tendency has been to write for a larger and larger public, and therefore the writer could only take for granted what his public had in common—that is, less and less. Since the Victorian age, there has also been apparent a contrary tendency—to write for a smaller and smaller public, but this tendency does not represent a simple *reaction*. The authors who (frequently derided) write for a small public are not writing for a more cultivated *class*, but for a heterogeneous number of peculiar individuals of various classes—for a kind of élite. The clerisy writing for the clerisy. Lord Elton[3] does not understand the cause of this.

So far, then, as 'men of letters' are concerned (using that term as loosely as possible) the immediate future does not offer any prospect of a clerisy appealing to a classless society, but writing for, and to some extent we hope in criticism of a lower-middle-class society. We may get two kinds of clerics; those who are too closely identified with their public, and those who are too isolated from any public.

ELITE AND ELITES

There is some danger of confusion, in speaking sometimes of the singular and sometimes of the plural. I suppose *an* élite is any category of men and women who because of their individual

[3] *St George or the Dragon; Towards a Christian Democracy* (1942).

capacities exercise significant power in any particular area. The clerisy is perhaps the most difficult of all élites to distinguish and define. It may be roughly defined as, at the top, those individuals who originate the dominant ideas, and alter the sensibility, of their time; if we recognize sensibility as well as 'ideas', we must include some painters and musicians, as well as writers. But when we say *originate*, we must include the new expression of an old idea; when we say *originate* and *alter* we must admit an element of representativeness, of giving expression to, what is already 'in the air'; and when we say *of their time*, we must recognize the frequent lapse of time before the detonation of a new idea appears to occur. I only add these qualifications, as a reminder that there are aesthetic, critical and intellectual problems here on to which we might easily get side-tracked.

ELITE AND CLASS AGAIN

The clerisy does, I think, tend to spring from a limited number of closely related classes. This may not, at any particular moment, be true of the most outstanding members of the clerisy; the clerisy would cease to be the clerisy, and would merely be a small and rather isolated class, if this were ever altogether true. If class and élite became the same, in the case of the clerisy, it would die of inbreeding. A family which can breed a cleric is not the same as a clerical family. Clerics spring from stock which is itself non-clerical, or not too clerical, but which is capable of producing and rearing clerics. Conversely, clerics do not always marry clerics (no orchids for Mr Humphry Ward[4]) and even if they do they do best to beget and bring forth non-clerics; the cleric of the third generation is not very healthy stock.

The cleric himself should be partly, though not altogether, emancipated from the class into which he is born; an out-caste.

---

[4] A possible reference to Humphry Ward, fellow of Brasenose and later on the staff of *The Times*, who in 1872 married Mary Augusta Arnold, grand-daughter of Dr Thomas Arnold. Mrs Ward wrote *Robert Elsmere* and a number of other novels.

He should, to some extent, be able to look upon, and mix with, all classes as an outsider; just as he should, to some extent, get out of his own century. These are counsels of perfection, to which none of us attain. He should also have a supra-national community of interest with clerics of other nations; so as to work against nationalism and racialism (provincialism) as he does against class.

CLERISY AND CULTURE

It would, I think, be an error to think of the clerisy as the exclusive trustees for, and transmitters of, culture. This implies certainly a very limited notion of culture. The maintenance of culture is a function of the whole people, each part having its own appropriate share of the responsibility; it is a function of classes rather than of élites. The clerisy can help to develop and modify it; they have a part to play, but only a part, in its transmission. If this sometimes appears the most important part, that is not to say that clerics are necessarily the most cultured people. (The artist is not necessarily a 'cultured person'; he provides nourishment for other people's culture.)

DIFFERENCES BETWEEN CLERICS

It is not the business of clerics to agree with each other; they are driven to each other's company by their common dissimilarity from everybody else, and by the fact that they find each other the most profitable people to disagree with, as well as to agree with. They differ from members of a class in having very different backgrounds from each other, and by not being united by prejudices and habits. They are apt to share a discontent with things as they are, but the ways in which they want to change them will be various and often completely opposed to each other. But beyond this, there are two kinds of division between clerics, one horizontal and one vertical. Horizontally, there are the *intellectuals* and the *emotives*. (I avoid here the difficult word 'imaginative', because this may be applied to either.) Intellectuals may be insensitive, and emotives may be intellectually feeble or irrational. Difficulties arise, not from this natural division, but from each type failing to recognize its own limitations: otherwise they profit by association with each other, except possibly musicians, who seem to live in a world apart, like some mathematical prodigies.

The point is, however, that we cannot ask for any common mind, or any common action, on the part of the clerics. They have a common function but this is below the level of conscious purposes. They have at least one common interest—an interest in the survival of the clerisy (cf Mr Joad's essay in the volume *Can Planning be Democratic?*) but they will have no agreement on how to promote this. Agreement and common action can only be by particular groups of clerics, and is most effectively exercised against some other group of clerics. When clerics can form a group in which formulated agreement is possible, it will be due to affinities which distinguish them from other clerics.

HIERARCHY OF THE CLERISY

I cannot find my copy of *La Trahison des clercs*, and I have not read the book since it first appeared. I remember that I did not think it so good as the author's *Belphegor*. My impression remains that Benda was an example of the Cretan Liar, and that he fell into treason while accusing others; but also that he did not distinguish different grades of *clerc*. The higher grades are those, whether philosophers or artists, who are concerned with the word (the discovery of truth or beauty) rather than with the audience, and the lower those who are more concerned with the audience—either to *influence* it or to *entertain* it, or both. (This does not exclude the possibility that a particular lower-grade cleric may be a *greater* man than a particular high-grade one.) Benda, as I remember, seemed to expect everybody to be a sort of Spinoza. Ideally, and often in practice, the work of the high-grade cleric first affects a lower-grade cleric—those who have some of the motives of the high and some of those of the low. *Man and Superman* may or may not be a popularization of ideas which Shaw (a middle-grade cleric) took from Samuel Butler (a higher-grade cleric—this irrespective of what we think of the value of his ideas or the unpleasantness of the man); and Shaw's dramatic invention gets down to the lowest dregs of clerisy in the plays of Noël Coward. (If you are going to refuse Coward the title of cleric you will have to draw a line somewhere and you will not find it easy to draw.) Whatever you think of Noël Coward, this general form of influence and dissemination is natural and right. Note, however, that the function of the lower-grade cleric is not simply to travesty or degrade what he gets from the higher, and when he does well, he makes influential the work of men who have done that work with no concern for influence—and that is the profoundest kind of influence. On the other hand, as all intellectual or artistic influence becomes modified, both by the brains which receive it and by its transformation in association with an increasing number of other influences, it ceases to be anything which could interest the man who started it. Philosophers, as well as artists, frequently disapprove violently of their disciples.

ECONOMIC AND SOCIAL DANGERS FOR THE CLERISY

Clerisy may be divided into the *employed* and the *unemployed*. By the former I mean those who are employed as clerics: among the unemployed, in this case, I include those who have independent incomes, those who earn a living in some way outside of their main interests (e.g. polishing lenses[5]), those who live off the sale of their clerical produce (books, pictures) and those who live as best they can. Obviously, it is not always easy to place a cleric wholly in one category or the other. A university stipendiary

[5]. The occupation of Spinoza.

may be interested in thinking and such activities, and bored by lecturing and tutoring: the question is the degree of which his paid activities support or interfere with his preferred clerical interests.

It is desirable that there should always be a proportion of employed and a proportion of unemployed clerics. From the point of view of the clerisy, some clerics need both the security and the opportunity to concentrate, which proper employment gives: it is also useful, both for the cleric and for the society in which he works, that he should have the prestige of official or institutional recognition. Other clerics need the independence of unemployment, either for the expression of unpopular views, or for the pursuit of some study the value of which is not immediately apparent to anyone but themselves. It is important also for society that some clerics should be able to do as they please. An excess of employed clerics incurs the danger of discouraging independence: official patronage of the arts in this way, certainly, may have the effect of suppressing everything except the highest level of the mediocre. On the other hand an excess of unemployed clerics is apt to be unsettling: when society produces a large number of unemployed clerical small fry, we have what is called the *intelligentsia*, expressing its discontent in subversive movements, and, in Cairo and such places, overturning trams.

In the present state of society, we are exposed to both of these dangers. In a planned and centralized society, some provision is going to be made for art and thought; so that the tendency may be for official positions to be made for the practitioners of such activities, especially as other means of picking up a living may become more difficult. It is also coming to be believed that a nation's art and thought have some political value in impressing other nations with a sense of that nation's importance, and stimulating an interest in the goods which it has to export, even books and pictures. But at the same time, with the vast extensions of education which are contemplated, there is a danger of producing an excessive number of half-baked clerics, beyond what the machine can find room for. The spread of education may also strengthen the pressure towards a low-grade culture (by which I mean, of course, something quite different from that part of total culture of which the lower orders are the proper guardians) which I mentioned earlier.

QUESTIONS

1. Does the term 'clerisy' convey enough meaning to be useful? Does it identify a type of activity such that we can say that a clerisy must exist in any civilized society? Can the function of the clerisy be defined? If so, to what extent is it fulfilled, and to what extent is it in defect, in this island at the present time?

2. Should the term, in extension, be made as inclusive or as exclusive as possible? Consider this in relation to well-known names in philosophy, science, the arts, and the variety stage.

3. If the term comprehends philosophy, science and the arts, each pretty inclusively, what statement can be made about *all* clerics except that they are concerned with 'culture'? But (apart from the *descriptive* interest of sociologists and anthropologists) is there any such thing as a direct concern with the *promotion* of culture? Are not clerics concerned with a number of different activities, the total of which, in so far as it happens to form an organic pattern, can be said to represent the culture of the society in which they operate?

4. Is the 'culture' of Britain declining in quality? If so, what are the evidences? What steps can or cannot be taken, so that the level can be raised without lowering the highest standards?

Revelation

Contribution to *Revelation*, edited by John Baillie and
Hugh Martin (1937)

WHAT I have to write is not an introduction to the essays in this
book, but an introduction to the subject; and it is because I am
not a theologian that I have been asked to contribute. I am not to
concern myself with the different forms in which men may hold
a doctrine of revelation, or with the consequences they may
deduce from it; either with the different theological systems, nor
with the different Christian communions. I am concerned with
the general differences between those who maintain a doctrine of
revelation and those who reject all revelation. I am assumed to
have an intimate and affectionate acquaintance with the limbo
and lower regions in which the secular world moves: a knowledge of objects towards which the theological mind is not often
directed. My qualification is the eye of the owl, not that of the
eagle.

I take for granted that Christian revelation is the only full
revelation; and that the fullness of Christian revelation resides in
the essential fact of the Incarnation, in relation to which all
Christian revelation is to be understood.

The division between those who accept, and those who deny,
Christian revelation I take to be the most profound division
between human beings. It does not merely go deeper than
divisions by political faith, divisions of class or race; it is different
in kind, and cannot be measured by the same scale. It need not
cancel these divisions, in so far as they represent principles of
union and not of discord. To deny the ties of blood and of
congeniality wholly would be to widen the chasm between
the Church and the World, and obstruct our indirect, still more

than our direct, missionary activity. The emphasis should be on what binds together Christians the world over, rather than on what divides them from others: so that Christian brotherhood should be not merely an idea held, a phrase spoken, but something consistently felt. Nevertheless, it is well for us to study what I may call the folk-lore and practices of the non-Christian world, for we shall not convert it unless we understand it.

The line to be drawn between the Christian and the non-Christian world is at present extremely difficult to draw. It is not enough, for our present purposes, to propound the wholesome reflexion that not all those who deny Christ are necessarily His enemies, and that many who profess Him are living by the World. The first remark to be made is that not even the *Oxford English Dictionary* definition of secularism is quite comprehensive:

> The doctrine that morality should be based solely on regard to the well-being of mankind in the present life, to the exclusion of all considerations drawn from belief in God or in a future state.

A doctrine of morality based not *solely*, but *primarily*, on regard to the well-being of mankind in the present life might also be classified as secularist. Also, what escapes the necessary concision of a dictionary definition, notions of what the 'present life' is, and accordingly of what 'well-being' is, may vary extremely; and we can only say that secularism *tends* to restrict the conception to what we call, still vaguely, 'material' well-being. And finally, a belief may be far from excluding considerations drawn from belief in God or in a future state, and yet, because of its conception of the nature of God, or of the future state, still be predominantly secularist.

The first error would be to identify secularism with what was called rationalism. I say 'what was called', because the word 'rationalism' can in general mean so much that in particular it is likely to mean something very much less, and to have accidental associations. The rationalism of the nineteenth century (that of the Rationalist Press Society) now seems very old-fashioned: the rationalism of Tyndall, Haeckel, and Mr Bernard Shaw. This antiquation is not the result of any religious revival but, I believe, of a further stage of religious decay. In countries like France where Christianity still means for the most part the Roman Catholic Church, and means a traditional Catholicism rather than one of individual conversion, the *non*-Christian forces are still *anti*-Christian, and therefore maintain a repudiation of anything that might be associated with religion. The sceptical state of mind is there still fundamentally Cartesian; and in spite of the appearance of Bergson—whose mind does not seem to me characteristically French—I am inclined to believe that philosophies which admit the inclusion of the irrational, or of anything which eludes rational grasp—such as *vitalism*—are more natural to non-'Latin' countries where the decay of Christianity has followed a different route. The English rationalism of the nineteenth century—not only that of the popular scientists but that of literary folk like George Eliot and Leslie Stephen—had more in common with Latin rationalism of today; though there was in it a rigid Puritan zeal, a confidence that the disappearance of Christianity would coincide with enlightenment and progress, which strikes us as not only obsolete but provincial.

In the English-speaking world of today, the rationalist is no longer quite so rationalistic. The change is partly, and evidently, due to further scientific discovery, and the growth of popular belief that no particular scientific theory can be accepted more than provisionally. One may cite such situations as that in which it is necessary for a physicist to hold two contradictory theories at once in order to be able to deal with different phenomena. A greater meekness is observed, and even a rush of scientists to stake out a little quasi-religious territory for themselves.

The formation of the Fabian Society in the latter years of the nineteenth century brought a bubbling-up to the intellectual surface of society of able men of imperfectly developed sensibilities. The kind of philosophy of life which Mr Shaw and Mr H. G. Wells had to offer no doubt seemed to them satisfactory for all because it was satisfactory to themselves. If you are so fortunate (from the point of view of this world) as to have no immortal longings, and are furthermore gifted with such fluency in writing as to be kept perpetually entertained by your own talents, you can be easily satisfied. But in some more recent writers we find a more defensive tone: they are anxious to assure their readers that the future, in a world in which science will replace religion, is *not* going to be dreary. The most readable of contemporary popular writers on science is Mr Gerald Heard. The epilogue to his *Science in the Making* contains the following remarkable statement:

Man, who has left to appetite the task of finding for him the worth of living, of being the sole sauce with which to give him the gusto to bite off and digest great chunks of the stubborn outer world, will find appetite sated almost before it can stir. Humanity will be bored. The mysterious word which first stole like a grey shadow over the court of *le Roi Soleil*, and then spread to all places where men of taste lived beyond the struggle for meats and mates, will percolate down from class to class till all are leisured, all are idly rich with a wealth of time on their hands, no people have ever possessed, ever been embarrassed with, before. If then mankind is not too weary of its life, to fly to making intentionally the accidents, the strains and anxieties which gave it thrills and spurs and sudden convictions that life is worthwhile (but which nature no longer makes for it), if it is not, through war, deliberately to break down into anarchy the order it has built up, it must find new interest and excitement. There is only one appetite from which this new stock of interest can spring and that is curiosity, the finest of the passions. Curiosity is impersonal and so can remain when all personal appetites have been paid off. Curiosity is not utilitarian and so can carry on when men are sated with means. Curiosity is inexhaustible and so can find fresh fields and new explorations when all the world that man can exploit is ordered, every sight has been seen and every power exercised.

I have said that this statement is remarkable. Readers will be reminded, by the turgid style rather than by the ill-constructed sentences, of that remarkable effusion of twenty years ago, Mr Bertrand Russell's *Free Man's Worship*. There is a considerable difference; there is twenty years' difference. Mr Heard's affirmation is still more incredible than Mr Russell's. *Curiosity the finest of the passions!* Vanity of vanities!

Another writer for whom I have considerable respect, Mr Herbert Read, has made a still more recent statement for himself which might be taken as an amendment, rather than a contradiction of Mr Heard's:

> Just as curiosity is the faculty which drives man to seek out the hidden structure of the external universe, thereby enabling him to build up that body of knowledge which we call science, so wonder is the faculty which dares man to create what has not before existed, which dares man to use his powers in new ways and for new effects. We have lost this sense of the word 'wonderful'—it is one of the most outworn clichés in the language. But actually 'wonder' is a better and more inclusive word than 'beauty', and what is full of wonder has the most compelling force over the imagination of men.

I adduce these quotations as evidence that the more reflective writers of this generation—those whose attention is not wholly taken up by prospective political and social reforms, and who therefore have the time to consider final ends—feel the need for assuring us that mankind still has something to live for. As the pleasures of iconoclasm subside, most of the idols having been demolished or removed to museums, the iconoclasts find it necessary to look about for objects to supply the needs that the idols satisfied. The result of offering an *activity*, such as 'curiosity' or 'wonder', to replace an *end*, is to make that activity appear a great deal more petty and trifling than it is to the person with religious faith. Curiosity or wonder, being exalted above its proper place, becomes a tedious activity, for it becomes merely a restless search for more sensation (it is not worthy of the name of experience) of the same kind. One would have thought that

Aristotle had said everything there was to be said on such matters, if the kinds of doctrine that Aristotle refuted had not flourished rather more luxuriantly after his time than before. A sound ethical doctrine is frequently replaced neither by one that is sounder, nor by one that is antithetical to it, but by one or more each of which selects some element of it to the exclusion of others.

A writer who is chronologically halfway between Shaw on the one hand and Heard and Read on the other, Mr Bertrand Russell, wrote a book called *The Conquest of Happiness*, which may be called a defence of mediocrity. It comes to the conclusion that so far as happiness depends upon oneself, and not upon circumstances, 'the recipe for happiness is a very simple one.' It is simple, of course, because Mr Russell simplified the problem to the degree of falsification. I do not propose to analyse his argument, in which is incorporated a great deal of advice, based partly upon the discovery by modern psychology of things that were known already, that is quite commonplace and perfectly acceptable. And he sometimes imagines that he is controverting traditional views when he is merely stating them in a partial way. For instance, he says:

> Professional moralists [*he does not say which*] have made too much of self-denial, and in so doing have put the emphasis in the wrong place. Conscious self-denial leaves a man self-absorbed and vividly aware of what he has sacrificed; in consequence it fails often of its immediate object and almost always of its ultimate purpose. What is needed is not self-denial, but that kind of direction of interest outward which will lead spontaneously and naturally to the same acts that a person absorbed in the pursuit of his own virtue could only perform by means of conscious self-denial.

The passage is interesting as a specimen of the confusion of thought into which secularists often fall. Christian ethics, in its true and complete form, has surely always 'put the emphasis' in quite another place from that of the 'professional moralists' of whom Mr Russell speaks. Christian morality is not an end but a means. Mr Russell simplifies his contrast by making it one simply between *inward* and *outward*. 'Professional morality' is for him a kind of egotism: the alternative is to be interested in things and people outside oneself. For the Christian there is a distinction of higher and lower, as well as of inner and outer: (the latter distinction belongs to a somewhat antiquated psychology which used the terms 'extrovert' and 'introvert'). And we may note two further points: one, that there seems to be a suggestion that self-denial is not merely a negative activity to be kept in its place, but that it is a repression to be discouraged; and second, that a traditionally or conventionally 'virtuous person' is one absorbed in the pursuit of his own virtue (undefined).

The reason why I have called Mr Russell's book a gospel of mediocrity is this: that because he finds that the ordinary man or woman is very rarely and not often seriously bothered about the destiny of man, but is in a state fluctuating between happiness and misery, which depends only on his material circumstances and his relations with his family and the people about him, the destiny of man is in consequence something of interest only to those few persons whose futile curiosity (another kind of curiosity than that which Mr Heard proposes) leads them to worry about such matters. Mr Russell sets up for our speculative acceptance a theory of life which he believes is that which the majority of men, so far as their self-interest is intelligent, live by. But when such an attitude is exposed in intellectual terms, it becomes something very different from what it is when it is merely lived out. We might say that it is a view of life which is perfectly tenable until it is made articulate. For once we have asked the question: what is the end of man? we have put ourselves beyond the possibility of being satisfied with the answer: 'there isn't any end, and the only thing to do is to be a nice person and get on with your neighbours.'

It is the difference between answering this question negatively, like Mr Russell, and finding an unsatisfactory answer, like Mr Heard or Mr Read, that marks a difference between two generations of secularists. On the simple political plane, of course, this difference is between the Socialists (rationalists) and the Communists. I should say rather, some Communists, because Communism is comprehensive enough to find a place for many who may be spiritually still Socialists: for those who see it as simply a more efficient machine than Socialism or Capitalism, for those who are moved by immediate humanitarian passions, as well as for those who seek it as a kind of salvation. It will be observed that although Communism does not attempt to answer the question: what is the end of man? and would I presume affirm such a question to be meaningless, it does offer an answer to another question: what is the end of the individual man or woman? and to many people this answer seems good enough. It is this answer which Communism is able to give to the question: what is the end of the individual? which goes to account for the 'conversion' of some notable individualist intellectuals, such as M. André Gide. There is a possible contrast to be drawn here between the conversion of intellectuals in the modern world to Christianity, and their conversion to Communism. The conversion to Christianity is apt to be due, I think, to a latent dissatisfaction with all secular philosophy, becoming, perhaps, with apparent suddenness, explicit and coherent.[1] A conversion to Communism, on the other hand, may be simply a flight from one extreme to avoid the other; with, on a deeper plane, a desire to satisfy repressed Christian impulses without embracing Christianity. I do not suggest that all cases of conversion can be accounted for in these ways; but I think that the suggestion I have just made would go far to account for M. André Gide. He found his *immoraliste* individualism leading nowhere, or at last to a dead end: and there seemed nothing to do, if he was to avoid Christianity, but to take the other extreme tack.[2] The satisfactions of individualism fail-ing, M. Gide turns to a doctrine which, while it has nothing to say to the question: what is the end of man? can say a good deal

[1] In this comparison I am deliberately disregarding the operation of grace in order to keep it to the secular plane.

[2] M. Gide's conversion to Communism has been presented as something involving an heroic sacrifice of his creative gifts. It might, of course, be retorted that possibly the exhaustion of M. Gide's creative gifts had something to do with his conversion to Communism.

about the self-surrender of the individual to society. The *âme collective* does duty for God. It is noteworthy that M. Gide (in spite of his distinguished connexion with Charles Gide) never took the slightest interest in economics, and still professes an utter ignorance of the subject. (He retains the charming frankness that has always been one of his most admirable qualities.[3]) I cannot help believing that M. Gide's motive was largely the *desire for his individual salvation*—which can remain a desire of something for oneself, even when it is a desire to escape from oneself. I am the more inclined to this belief because M. Gide's writings have always seemed to me to belong to a class of literature of which they are neither the first nor the last example: that in which the author is moved partly by the desire to justify himself, and partly by the desire to cure himself. The greatest authors have never written for these reasons; but among this class is included much of the best of the second order of writing.[4]

The Marxist mysticism is not the only secular mysticism that has been propagated in our time. I do not intend to discuss racial or imperial mysticism, as it does not seem philosophically to merit very much attention. The most remarkable, the most ambitious attempt to erect a secular philosophy of life in our

---

[3] According to the *compte rendu* of a debate which took place a few years ago between M. Gide and some of his non-Communist critics, he professed to have been moved largely by humanitarian motives. I would not depreciate these, but they do not seem quite adequate by themselves.

[4] For a fervent expression of the desire for salvation by escape from individuality, see an essay by Mr J. Middleton Murry in a symposium called *Marxism* (Chapman and Hall, 1935). Mr Murry may have modified his views since and, even if not, might wish to rewrite some of his pages: for on p. 105 he says: 'at the heart of Marxism lies a grim effort at "depersonalization", which unless a man has undergone, I do not believe he will ever be a Marxist save in name. Of course, this is true only for the member of "bourgeois society" who becomes a Marxist . . .' But at the end of the same paragraph he says: 'That grim effort at depersonalization, of which I have spoken, is just as incumbent upon any proletarian who wants to be a Marxist as upon any bourgeois.' Mr Murry tells us emphatically that the individual is an illusion, and that 'his sole concrete reality is that of a cell of social organism, governed by unconscious laws'. The point is that Mr Murry has started with a notion of the 'individual' which is not Christian, in order to end by denying the existence of the individual. He derives Marxism from Spinoza.

time—though of course not the most influential—is that of the late Irving Babbitt. In a survey like this, Babbitt deserves more attention than any of the other writers whom I have mentioned or shall mention. In the first place, Babbitt's motive was aware-ness of, alarm at, the ills of the modern secular world; and his work as a whole constitutes the most complete and thorough diagnosis of the malady, as it shows itself in literature, in educa-tion, in politics and philosophy, that has been made. His learning was not only prodigious but organized so as at every point to reinforce the structure of his thought. He saw connexions that no other mind would have perceived. He was not a system-builder. What makes him unique is that, while himself a disbe-liever, even an opponent of revealed religion, he attacked the foundations of secularism more deeply and more comprehen-sively than any other writer of our time. His mind, on its periphery, touching questions and philosophies of our time, might be the mind of a Christian; and except from a Christian standard, I do not see how we can object to his conclusions. We have to penetrate to the interior to find cause for dissatisfaction.

I have written elsewhere, and some years ago, about the inadequacy of Babbitt's doctrine of the 'higher will' and the 'inner check', and I do not propose to repeat my criticism of Babbitt on these points. But a posthumous essay which was published last year (*The Dhammapada: Translated from the Pali with an Essay on Buddha and the Occident*) gives occasion for a review having a closer bearing upon our subject. The problem is why Babbitt, with such a mind and equipment as, it would seem, could only be supported by Christianity, should have turned to Primitive Buddhism (Hinayana) instead. But first it will help us if we can form some conclusion about what he made of Buddh-ism.

I think that careful attention to this important and interesting essay will disclose a steady, unconscious desire to evade Christian conclusions at any cost, even at the cost of what may seem to others than the author rather important features of Buddhism. One of the reasons why Buddhism appeals to him is apparently his hostility to Platonic ideas, and his dislike of the

Platonic influence upon Christian theology. 'Buddha is so disconcerting to us', he says, 'because doctrinally he recalls the most extreme of our Occidental philosophers of the flux, and at the same time, by the type of life at which he aims, reminds us rather of the Platonist and of the Christian.' Yet he recognizes quite clearly that contrast between the flux and the eternal is quite as vital to Buddhism as to Christianity, for he says later: 'According to Buddha, anything that is impermanent is not only unreal but finally illusory.' Throughout the essay he insists upon this difference between Buddhism and Christianity: that in Buddhism one can come to a genuine supernaturalism on 'strictly experimental' grounds, for reasons that are 'not metaphysical but practical', by knowledge of 'immediate data of consciousness', on 'psychological grounds', by a 'practical and psychological method'. It is worth while discovering what can, and cannot, be affirmed on 'strictly experimental' grounds, or what it means to be a 'critical and experimental supernaturalist'. When Babbitt says 'supernaturalist', he does not mean a person who believes in miracles: on that point he is rather guarded. What is specifically supernatural, he says, about Buddha and other religious teachers such as St Francis, is 'their achievement of certain virtues'; of which virtues he puts humility at the head. It turns out a little later that what we have to do with is not humility, but 'the psychic equivalent' of humility, that is, a will that transcends the cosmic order. And he affirms the existence of a 'quality of will' peculiar to man as one of the immediate data of consciousness. He is certain of this, and equally certain that the soul and the existence of God are not immediate data of consciousness. Yet he does not consider the question whether we can talk about immediate data of consciousness unless, as is far from the case, we generally agree as to what they are: otherwise, one man's data may turn out to be another man's constructions.

According to Babbitt's scheme, the primacy of a certain 'quality of will' distinguishes Buddhism. But at this point he is not apparently contrasting Buddhism with Christianity, but with the views of 'Western philosophers' from Descartes down. And he admits that this Buddhistic 'quality of will . . . has been almost inextricably bound up in the Occident with the doctrine of divine grace and has been obscured in direct proportion to the decline of this doctrine'.

We might complain here that since his Buddhism is by assumption a pure Buddhism, uncorrupted by the practices and doctrines of later times, he ought to contrast it with the equally pure Christianity of whatever period he chose; and that we should not be distracted by corruptions or perversions of Christian doctrine, if we are not allowed to consider those of Buddhism. But while this excellent quality of the will has been obscured in the Occident by the decline of the doctrine of grace, yet it is also the will's association with this doctrine that Babbitt objects to. For grace does not appeal to the practical, experimental, realistic mind; although this same practical mind can accept the idea of the 'higher self' as a self 'that one possesses in common with other men'. At this point Babbitt would seem to be very near to Mr Murry and the mystical Communists: but it is the 'individualism' of Buddha that most powerfully attracts him. He observes:

> The person who assumes a genuinely critical attitude is finally forced to accept in some form or other the maxim that man is the measure of all things. If one is told in the words of Plato that not man but God is the measure of all things, the obvious reply is that man nowhere perhaps gives his own measure so clearly as in his conception of God ...

To which the obvious reply is that this may be an obvious reply, but is a smart and sophistical retort without being an answer. If man gives his own measure in his conception of God, then there must be a God in relation to whom man's conception is measured.

There are moments, indeed, in which Babbitt appears to be offering Buddhism for the serious consideration of the Christian, not as a preferable alternative, but as a complement.

> The true Buddhist, like the true Christian, takes a gloomy view of the unconverted man.

His paradox of true self-love, interpreted in the light of renunciation, does not turn out so very differently from the Christian paradox of dying that one may live.

In general, a collateral benefit of any comprehension one may achieve of Buddha is that it will help one to a better understanding of Christ.

Religion also looks upon life as a process of adjustment. This process as envisaged by the Christian is summed up once for all in Dante's phrase: 'In his will is our peace.' A reading of works like *The Dhammapada* suggests that the psychological equivalent of this form of adjustment was not unknown to Buddha.

One might remark, about the last of these quotations, that it is not proved that there can be any 'psychological equivalent'; and it leads us further to remark that Babbitt sometimes appears to be unaware of differences as well as of resemblances between Buddhism and Christianity. His observations about Christian mysticism suggest that there is perhaps one gap in his immense reading; certainly in his understanding. But his relative estimate of the two religions may be gauged from the following:

It would seem desirable, then, that those who object on either humanistic or religious grounds to the overreaching attitude of scientific naturalists should not burden themselves with any unnecessary metaphysical or theological baggage, and that their appeal should be to experience rather than to some counter dogma.

Which must be taken as a downright rejection of revelation.

Now, one very remarkable fact strikes the reader the moment he has finished this essay. When Babbitt speaks of Christianity he is apt to be thinking of some of the decayed forms of religiosity that he had seen about him, yet he is concerned with a faith that men had been professing to live by during nearly two thousand years. When he speaks of Buddhism, he is dealing with a refined abstraction, with the texts of the master's sayings. He is comparing not Buddha and Christ, or Buddhism and Christianity, but Buddha and Christianity. And there is a still more remarkable oversight. I do not think that his argument, or rather persuasion, is so much invalidated by his rejection of what came after Buddha, as by his ignoring of what came before. Buddha may be regarded as a reformer of a religion that had been in existence for a long time before him, and one of the assumptions of that religion was the doctrine of reincarnation. Babbitt says in passing: 'A Buddha is supposed to be immediately aware not merely of his own karma, but, at will, of the karma of others.' But he does not tell us whether he himself believes in karma and in reincarnation, or in the doctrine that there have been many Buddhas. One would like to know whether these are questions of 'unnecessary metaphysical and theological baggage', or of experience. Whether the Buddha himself believed in these doctrines is not quite the point either: the point is that reincarnation was so deep in the mentality of his hearers as to be a category of their thought, and that his teaching assumes its truth. And it is as essential to Buddhism as the future states of heaven and hell are to Christianity.

'Knowledge in matters religious waits upon will.' That seems to me to state, though perhaps one-sidedly, a very important truth. The more intelligent and sensitive the secularist is, the more clearly manifest in him is the deflection of will. And that sentence also I have quoted from Babbitt's essay on Buddhism.

I suggest that the Buddhism of Irving Babbitt is not simply a *purified* Buddhism, essence of Buddhism freed from all gross superstitions and made palatable for the intellectual and cultivated modern man: but that it is an artificial Buddhism—not only purified but *canned*; separated from all the traditional ways of behaving and feeling which went to make it a living religion in its own environments, which made it a religion possible for every level of intelligence and sensibility from the highest to the lowest. It therefore has something in common with the *psychological mysticism* that is a phenomenon of decadence rather than of growth. This is the mysticism which seeks contact with the sources of supernatural power, divorced from religion and theology; the mysticism which must always be suspect, and which sometimes springs up in cults whose aims are not far removed from those of magic.

It is significant that this psychological mysticism has recently appeared in the work of a writer very far removed from Irving Babbitt in attitude, a writer the majority of whose works Babbitt would probably have associated with much of what he disapproved. The mixture of violent prejudice with sympathetic interest in Christianity displayed in the writings of Babbitt has a curious analogue in the writings of Mr Aldous Huxley. Most of our Communists show indifference, rather than hostility, to Christianity: an indifference only possible on a foundation of ignorance, insensibility and incuriosity. Mr Huxley is neither ignorant, insensitive nor incurious; he has attempted to maintain an intelligent scepticism in a world of increasing barbarism. He has often written about Christianity, breathing a kind of low fire and chilly fury that seem to indicate that it has some interest for him. It is interesting, therefore, after considering Babbitt on the *Dhammapada*, to read the last page of Mr Huxley's Peace Pamphlet (*What Are You Going to Do About It?*). Here we find him advocating the practice of 'meditation' (to which Babbitt also was devoted) specifically for the purpose of bringing about the Will to Peace.

> The sources of the will lie below the level of consciousness in a mental region where intellect and feeling are largely inoperative. Whatever else they may be—and many theological and psychological theories have been elaborated in order to explain their nature and their mode of action—religious rites, prayer and meditation are devices for affecting the sources of the will. It is a matter of empirical experience that regular meditation on, say, courage or peace often helps the meditator to be brave and serene. Prayer for moral strength and tenacity of purpose is in fact quite often answered. Those who, to express in symbolic action their attachment to a cause, take part in impressive ceremonies and rites, frequently come away strengthened in their power to resist temptations and make sacrifices for the cause. There is good evidence that the prac-

tice of some kind of spiritual exercise in common is extremely helpful to those who undertake it.... Meditation is a psychological technique whose efficacy does not depend on previous theological belief. It can be successfully practised by anyone who is prepared to take the necessary trouble.

This is a very interesting statement. I am certainly not one to deny that 'meditation is a psychological technique whose efficacy does not depend on previous theological belief.' I only maintain that if it neither depends on previous theological belief nor leads towards it, then it is a technique that must be very suspect indeed. It may turn out to be merely an occult means of getting one's own way; it may foster the *libido dominandi*. Mr Huxley would be the last to deny this; only he would insist that to meditate to bring about peace is obviously to meditate for a good cause. So far, so good: but from a Christian point of view—from any religious point of view—it cannot be an ultimate good cause, inasmuch as peace itself (the peace of this world) is not an end but a means. There is apt to be impurity of motives in our *natural* devotion even to such a good cause as peace; and in the effort to purify our motives towards peace, the effort to isolate for contemplation the essential idea of peace, we must, I think, be led to the final theological problem of the end of man. Otherwise, it is an endeavour to employ great and unknown forces for immediate and inadequate ends: and that seems to me to be putting ourselves in the utmost spiritual danger. It is an even greater temptation than that of the eudemonism, possibly ataraxy, to which the meditation of Babbitt might lead.

I have not, however, introduced the mysticism of Mr Huxley for its own interest, and still less in order to discuss the problem of peace, but as a bit of evidence for the thesis that secularism today is not a solid force of disciplined troops, but a varied host of allegiances. And I might say at this point that I do not mean by secularism primarily the various distractions from the Christian life, the various temptations to live on a simply animal level, which occasion so much distress to the faithful. I am not concerned with the cinema, or the press, or the wireless, or the degrading influences of a mechanized civilization. These are serious enough, but they constitute a minor problem. They represent merely the contemporary form—though it may be a form more powerful and oppressive than any before—of the permanent force of the world against which the spirit must always struggle. I am concerned with the ideas, the philosophies, however inchoate, which either tolerate these things or fail to oppose them in the right way. For we must remember that almost every secular philosophy or social system, even those which we must regard as definitely hostile, is itself opposed to *some* of the features of contemporary society that we ourselves condemn.

The fact is that the situation of belief in the modern world is more analogous to that of the later Roman Empire than to any other period that we know. And one of the features of resemblance is the psychological mysticism of which I have been speaking.

There are many other philosophies individually worthy of discussion; and of course this paper would be neater if I did not confine myself almost altogether to examples from England and America, but considered men individually equally important in other countries. I know that I ought to have something to say about Stefan George, and certainly Max Scheler and possibly Friedrich Gundolf; and I ought to have given a succinct historical account of how things came to be as they are, without failing to give due space to Schopenhauer, Wagner and Nietzsche. I should touch upon Schleiermacher and Feuerbach, and I should have a long footnote about Logical Positivism, speculating how much it owes to G. E. Moore on the one hand, and Brentano, Husserl, Meinong and Heidegger on the other. But this is a paper, and not a book; and it is a paper written for a special occasion. It seems to me therefore proper to use the material that is ready in my mind, without either taking time to refresh my memory of authors whom I have read only once, or still less mug up works that I have never read at all. So before making my concluding observations, I shall consider one man who cannot be omitted, an

Englishman who cannot be duplicated or replaced by a specimen from any other country, whose position is unique, and whose peculiar attitude towards Christianity does not seem to me to have been quite correctly estimated. That is D. H. Lawrence.

The point is that the will to get out from Christianity into a religion of one's own operated in Lawrence as it operated in Babbitt. The extreme differences between the two men (how they would have disliked each other) account easily for their decamping in quite opposite directions; but there is a certain similarity in the motive. Both men sprang from environments which (however different in other ways) gave them an early experience of Christianity at anything but its best; and they failed ever completely to see Christianity as anything but the Christianity that entered into their early and important sensitive experience. Less passionate and powerful men, in a similar way on their own level, have gone through life unable to identify Christianity with anything more than the unpleasant smell of their school chapel, or a particular preceptor whom they disliked. We have found in Babbitt a suspiciously determined will not to be taken in—a will to be 'modern', 'empirical' and 'experimental' at all costs, even the cost of using such words only as emotional exclamations. Lawrence is less complicated and in some respects less interesting. His will against Christianity is easier to understand. For Babbitt was by nature an educated man, as well as a highly well-informed one: Lawrence, even had he acquired a great deal more knowledge and information than he ever came to possess, would always have remained uneducated. By being 'educated' I mean having such an apprehension of the contours of the map of what has been written in the past, as to see instinctively where everything belongs, and approximately where anything new is likely to belong; it means, furthermore, being able to allow for all the books one has not read and the things one does not understand—it means some understanding of one's own ignorance. With these two odd handicaps—the will against Christianity that was a residue of childhood and adolescence, and the temperament of *un*education—Lawrence started out on a lifelong search for a religion.

Whatever his disadvantages, a man of the ability of Lawrence, and with such an addiction, can be of very great value indeed; and it is as an investigator of the religious life—as a kind of *contemplative* rather than a theologian—that he seems to me to take a high place with most right. People have deplored the spoiling of the remarkable novelist of *Sons and Lovers* for the making of a medicine man; but much as I admire that rather sickly and morally unintelligible book, I find the medicine man much more important than the novelist. Mr Aldous Huxley, in his admirable preface to Lawrence's collected letters,[5] says 'Lawrence was always and unescapably an artist.' He does not seem to me an artist at all, but a man with a sketch-book: his poetry, very interesting amateur work, is only notes for poems. Mr Huxley says significantly a little later: 'the fact of his being an artist explains a life which seems, when you forget it, inextricably strange.' The truth is, of course, that an artist needs to live a commonplace life if he is to get his work done—a life far more of routine, and indeed less 'inextricably strange' than that of a politician or a stockbroker. An artist may have elements in his composition that drive him towards excesses of one kind or another, but a failure to keep these in hand leads to a failure in his art. But I think of Lawrence neither as an artist, nor as a man who failed to be an artist; I think of him, as I have suggested, as a researcher into religious emotion. And unless we see him as this, we are apt to attach too much importance to his views on sex and on society, to his psychological extravaganzas, and to personal peculiarities which may account for his aberrations. With the criticism of Lawrence's particular doctrines—his feminism,[6] his *âme collective*, his unconscious—I am for the most part in agreement with Mr Wyndham Lewis in the section of his *Paleface* that he devotes to Lawrence. But I think that something valuable remains, if we know how to use it.

In the oscillation—of which I shall speak presently—of secular philosophies between antithetical extremes, there is one pair

---

[5] Reprinted in Mr Huxley's recent volume of essays, *The Olive Tree*.

[6] The most objectionable feature of *Lady Chatterley's Lover* is surely the view of the male as merely an instrument for the purposes of the female.

of opposites which it is pertinent to mention at this point. The human mind is perpetually driven between two desires, between two dreams each of which may be either a vision or a nightmare: the vision and nightmare of the material world, and the vision and nightmare of the immaterial. Each may be in turn, or for different minds, a refuge to which to fly, or a horror from which to escape. We desire and fear both sleep and waking; the day brings relief from the night, and the night brings relief from the day; we go to sleep as to death, and we wake as to damnation. We move, outside of the Christian faith, between the terror of the purely irrational and the horror of the purely rational. Lawrence had a really extraordinary capacity for being exacerbated by the modern world of enlightenment and progress, whether in a Midland mining village or in metropolitan intellectual society. This world was his nightmare; he wanted a world in which religion would be real, not a world of church congresses and religious newspapers, not even a world in which a religion could be *believed*,[7] but a world in which religion would be something deeper than belief, in which life would be a kind of religious behaviourism. Hence the prancing Indians, who, in *Mornings in Mexico*, inspired some of his finest and most brilliant writing. He wished to go as low as possible in the scale of human consciousness, in order to find something that he could assure himself was *real*.

The attempt is fundamentally chimerical. We do not feel that Lawrence really got inside the skin of his Hopis, nor would we wish him to do so, because he was a civilized and sensitively conscious man, and his Indians, one feels, are pretty stupid. He merely gave a marvellous record of how the Indians affected

---

[7] Compare, for a very different attitude to a similar apprehension, the words of Dom John Chapman (*Spiritual Letters*, p. 47) '. . . the *corresponding trial* of our contemporaries seems to be the *feeling of not having any faith*; not temptations against any particular article (usually), but a mere feeling that religion is not true. It is an admirable purgative, just as the eighteenth century one was; it takes all pleasure out of spiritual exercises, and strips the soul naked. It is very unpleasant.' Lawrence saw no need for standing up to this. It would be unfair to say that he ran away; because it never occurred to him that there was any other course to take.

Lawrence. Yet his mistaken attempt was the result of an aware-
ness of something very important. He was aware that religion is
not, and can never survive as, simply a code of morals. It has not
even much meaning to say that religion is 'good'. Other things
are good or bad in relation to one's religion. If (I think he would
have said) you find you can only accept an 'evil' religion, then for
God's sake do, for that is far nearer the truth than not having any.
For what the evil religion has in common with the good is more
important than the differences; and it is more important really to
feel terror than to sing comminatory psalms. So he set himself,
by an immense effort of will—the same effort that the Christian
has to make towards a different end—to believe in nature spirits,
and to try to worship stocks and stones. And with the same
perseverance he set himself to an attitude of scepticism towards
science, for he saw that science only provides a relative truth, and
as we cannot know the relations, we do better—the contemporary mind being what it is—to deny it altogether than to accept it
as an absolute which it is not.

The religion of Lawrence can be a useful criterion for us in
testing the reality of our own faith: it can serve as a constant
reminder that Christianity is frightening, frightful and scandal-
ous to that secular mind which we are all compelled to some
extent to share. But for itself, it remains on the level of secularism, because it remains a religion of power and magic. Or rather,
the religion which Lawrence would have liked to achieve is a
religion of power and magic, of control rather than propitiation.
What he, being a civilized man, actually arrived at, was, of
course, only a religion of autotherapy. It was like the restless
search of the hypochondriac for a climate in which he can be
cured, or in which at least he can bear his ailments more easily.
Perhaps there is this motive in all of us, but if so, at least we can
hope that our being aware of it helps to keep it in its place. We
can cry, *Thou son of David, have mercy on me*, but we can be healed
only if our faith is stronger even than our desire to be healed.

The purpose of this brief, and no doubt apparently capricious,
review has been primarily to make the point that we are not

suffering today simply from 'loss of faith'—a loss of faith which brings with it inexorably a lowered vitality—but from a strong and positive misdirection of the will. I have been concerned chiefly with individualistic misdirections of will, not with the collective misdirections of a political nature; but the latter must be kept in mind also. I should now like to detail what seem to me the principal characteristics of philosophies without revelation.[8]

The first characteristic is *instability*. Were there a science of social psychology, it would no doubt provide a set of convenient terms in which to explain the necessity of impermanence. But we may say that any philosophy of life which is the construct of any individual mind, must be conditioned by a great deal of which that individual is unconscious. A man is never pure mind, his mind is conditioned by his sensibility and his physical constitution. It is observable that while impersonality of thought is at best only an ideal towards which some approximation can be reached, in modern philosophy divorced from theology this ideal itself has been surrendered. We are able even to have the *aesthetic* attitude towards philosophy, so that the work of an individual philosopher can be enjoyed, not for whatever in it may be true, but as an artistic presentation of the personality of the philosopher. There are, of course, group-personalities apparent in philosophy as well as individual personalities—so that it is said that Oxford and Cambridge philosophers are unable to understand each other. This is in part a healthy reaction against the 'lonely thinker' (Spinoza polishing lenses, the Sage of Koenigsberg, Marx in the British Museum), for of all thinkers the lonely one is likely to be the most controlled by the part of himself he knows nothing about. But however much we get together, we can by human means alone arrive only at the kind of fixity and unanimity of belief which might be attributed to a hive of bees. Ultimately, apart from revelation, there would seem to be no criterion of philosophic credibility.

[8] One might mention at this point the characteristics of those religions whic' are non-historical. But it does not fall within the scope of this paper, which concerned with secularism, to expound the view (implicit in what I say) t' revelation in the complete sense is the Incarnation.

The second characteristic is *recurrence*. The same philosophies tend to reappear again and again, sometimes by deliberate revival, but perhaps more often unconsciously. We easily believe that something is quite new when it is merely a new form, adapted to place and time, of some doctrine of antiquity. Those who yearn for an earthly paradise have to maintain that the key to human problems has been found for the first time.

The third characteristic is involved in the second: it is *the tendency* of each extreme philosophy *to evoke an opposite*, and sometimes to turn into it by an imperceptible metamorphosis. Thus you get an oscillation between individualism and collectivism; between rationalism and intuitivism; and an immoderate humanitarianism may lead to cruelty and tyranny. All these things spring from titanism, or the attempt to build a purely human world without reliance upon grace.

The fourth characteristic of secular philosophies is *immediate results*. It is easy to invent philosophies that will appear to the uneducated to be more promising than Christianity: which will appear more feasible, valid either for the inventors individually, or for a limited group or under transient conditions of time and place. Secular philosophies must inevitably, in the atmosphere of the modern world, have a seductiveness with which Christianity cannot compete. They are always presented as new, and as capable of setting things right at once.

We must remember also that the choice between Christianity and secularism is not simply presented to the innocent mind, *anima semplicetta*, as to an impartial judge capable of choosing the best when the causes have both been fully pleaded. The whole tendency of education (in the widest sense—the influences playing on the common mind in the forms of 'enlightenment') has for a very long time to form minds more and more adapted to secularism, less and less equipped to apprehend the doctrine of grace and its consequences. Even in works of Christian apologetic the assumption is sometimes that of the secular apologetic which presents the Christian faith as a

[...] doctrine of the damnation of unbaptized infants has been [...] recent times simply because it is repugnant. But the

190

preferable alternative to secular philosophy, which fights secular-ism on its own ground, is making a concession which is a preparation for defeat. Apologetic which proceeds from part to part of the body of Christian belief, testing each by itself accord-ing to secular standards of credibility, and which attempts to constitute Christian belief as a body of acceptable parts, so as to end by placing the least possible burden upon faith, seems to me to be a reversal of the proper method. Should we not first try to apprehend the meaning of Christianity as a whole, leading the mind to contemplate first the great gulf between the Christian mind and the secular habits of thought and feeling into which, so far as we fail to watch and pray, we all tend to fall? When we have appreciated the awfulness of this difference, we are in a better position to examine the body of our belief analytically, and consider what is permanent truth, and what is transient or mis-taken. As even the disciples, during the life of our Lord and immediately after His death and resurrection, suffered from occasional lapses of faith, what are we to expect of a world in which the will has been powerfully and increasingly misdirected for a long time past? What a discursive reading of the literature of secularism, over a number of years, leads me to believe, how-ever, is that the religious sentiment—which can only be com-pletely satisfied by the complete message of revelation—is simply suffering from a condition of repression painful for those in whom it is repressed, who yearn for the fulfilment of belief, although too ashamed of that yearning to allow it to come to consciousness.

---

development of the state of mind to which the doctrine is repugnant must itself be examined before we can accept it with confidence; and the question of the repugnance of a doctrine is not the same as that of its truth. This is perhaps the extreme case, but it is obviously very dangerous to rely on a sentiment of recent growth, especially when the higher religious emotions have certainly tended atrophy or occlusion.